LIST OF VOLUMES PUBLISHED IN THIS SERIES

Each bound in clothette, 1s. net

(No. 62 is in cloth, 2s. net)

1. **First and Last Things.** By H. G. WELLS.
2. **Education.** By HERBERT SPENCER.
3. **The Riddle of the Universe.** By ERNST HAECKEL.
4. **Humanity's Gain from Unbelief.** By CHARLES BRADLAUGH.
5. **On Liberty.** By JOHN STUART MILL.
6. **A Short History of the World.** By H. G. WELLS.
7. **Autobiography of Charles Darwin.**
8. **The Origin of Species.** By CHARLES DARWIN. (6th Copyright edition.)
9. **Twelve Years in a Monastery.** By JOSEPH MCCABE.
10. **History of Modern Philosophy.** By A. W. BENN.
11. **Gibbon on Christianity.** From Gibbon's *Decline and Fall of the Roman Empire.*
12. **The Descent of Man.** Pt. I and concluding Chapter Pt. III. By CHARLES DARWIN.
13. **History of Civilization in England.** By H. T. BUCKLE. Vol. I.
14 & 15. **Anthropology.** By SIR EDWARD B. TYLOR. Two vols.
16. **Iphigenia.** Two plays by EURIPIDES. English version by C. B. BONNER, M.A
17. **Lectures and Essays.** By THOMAS HENRY HUXLEY.
18. **The Evolution of the Idea of God.** By GRANT ALLEN.
19. **An Agnostic's Apology.** By SIR LESLIE STEPHEN, K.C.B.
20. **The Churches and Modern Thought.** By VIVIAN PHELIPS.
21. **Penguin Island.** By ANATOLE FRANCE.
22. **The Pathetic Fallacy.** By LLEWELYN POWYS.
23. **Historical Trials (a Selection).** By SIR JOHN MACDONELL.
24. **A Short History of Christianity.** By JOHN M. ROBERTSON.
25. **The Martyrdom of Man.** By WINWOOD READE.
26. **Head Hunters ; Black, White, and Brown.** By A. C. HADDON.
27. **The Evidence for the Supernatural.** By IVOR LL. TUCKETT.
28. **The City of Dreadful Night, and Other Poems.** By JAMES THOMSON (" B.V.").
29. **In the Beginning.** By PROF. SIR G. ELLIOT SMITH, F.R.S.
30. **Adonis ; A Study in the History of Oriental Religion.** By SIR JAMES G. FRAZER.
31. **Our New Religion.** By the RT. HON. H. A. L. FISHER.
32. **On Compromise.** By JOHN VISCOUNT MORLEY, O.M., P.C.
33. **History of the Taxes on Knowledge.** By COLLET DOBSON COLLET.
34. **The Existence of God.** By JOSEPH MCCABE.
35. **The Story of the Bible.** By MACLEOD YEARSLEY, F.R.C.S.
36. **Savage Survivals.** By J. HOWARD MOORE.
37. **The Revolt of the Angels.** By ANATOLE FRANCE.
38. **The Outcast.** By WINWOOD READE.
39. **Penalties Upon Opinion.** By HYPATIA BRADLAUGH BONNER.
40. **Oath, Curse, and Blessing.** By E. CRAWLEY.

41. **Fireside Science.** By Sir E. Ray Lankester, F.R.S. Prepared by Surgeon Rear-Admiral Beadnell.
42. **History of Anthropology.** By A. C. Haddon.
43. **The World's Earliest Laws.** By Chilperic Edwards.
44. **Fact and Faith.** By Prof. J. B. S. Haldane.
45. **Men of the Dawn.** By Dorothy Davison.
46. **The Mind in the Making.** By James Harvey Robinson.
47. **The Expression of the Emotions in Man and Animals.** By Charles Darwin. Revised and Abridged by Surg. Rear-Adml. Beadnell.
48. **Psychology for Everyman (and Woman).** By A. E. Mander.
49. **The Religion of the Open Mind.** By A. Gowans Whyte.
50. **Letters on Reasoning.** By John M. Robertson.
51. **The Social Record of Christianity.** By Joseph McCabe.
52. **Five Stages of Greek Religion.** By Prof. Gilbert Murray.
53. **The Life of Jesus.** By Ernest Renan.
54. **Selected Works of Voltaire.** Translated by Joseph McCabe.
55. **What Are We to Do with Our Lives?** By H. G. Wells.
56. **Do What You Will.** By Aldous Huxley.
57. **Clearer Thinking : Logic for Everyman.** By A. E. Mander.
58. **History of Ancient Philosophy.** By A. W. Benn.
59. **Your Body : How it is Built and How it Works.** By Dr. D. Stark Murray.
60. **What is Man?** By Mark Twain.
61. **Man and His Universe.** By John Langdon-Davies.
62. **First Principles.** By Herbert Spencer. (Double Vol., cloth 2s.)
63. **Rights of Man.** By Thomas Paine. With Introduction by G. D. H. Cole.
64. **This Human Nature.** By Charles Duff.
65. **Dictionary of Scientific Terms.** By Surgeon Rear-Admiral C. M. Beadnell.
66. **A Book of Good Faith.** Selections from the Works of Montaigne, chosen by Gerald Bullett.
67. **The Universe of Science.** By Prof. H. Levy.
68. **Liberty To-Day.** Revised Edition. By C. E. M. Joad.
69. **The Age of Reason.** By Thomas Paine.
70. **The Fair Haven.** By Samuel Butler. With Introduction by Gerald Bullett.
71. **A Candidate for Truth.** Passages from Emerson, arranged by Gerald Bullett.
72. **A Short History of Women.** By John Langdon-Davies.

NATURAL CAUSES AND
SUPERNATURAL SEEMINGS

NATURAL CAUSES

AND

SUPERNATURAL

SEEMINGS

BY

HENRY MAUDSLEY, M.D.

LONDON:

WATTS & CO.,

5 & 6 JOHNSON'S COURT, FLEET STREET, E.C.4

Abridged edition, first issued in Thinker's Library 1939.

Printed and Published in Great Britain by C. A. Watts & Co. Limited,
5 & 6 Johnson's Court, Fleet Street, London, E.C.4

BIOGRAPHICAL NOTE*

HENRY MAUDSLEY, who came of a yeoman farmer family long settled near Settle, Yorkshire, was born in 1835. His adoption of a medical career seems to have been due to the interest taken in him by his uncle, Dr. Bateson, who, after Henry had matriculated at the University of London, arranged for him to be apprenticed to the apothecary of University College Hospital. Although he was reputed to be lacking in diligence and to be more interested in cricket than in his work, he had a brilliant record as a student at University College, winning ten gold medals, taking first place in most class competitions, and receiving the University Scholarship and the gold medal in surgery when he graduated M.B. in 1856. These triumphs, however, he held in slight esteem, regarding them less as proofs of real knowledge than as indications of accurate memory. This estimate was as just as it was modest, since he enjoyed an exceptionally good visual memory, which enabled him to reproduce long passages of text with a fidelity independent of the degree of understanding.

After acting as house surgeon at University College Hospital under Mr. Quain, Dr. Maudsley planned to enter the Indian Medical Service. As experience in mental diseases was necessary for entrance to the I.M.S., he took an appointment at Essex County Asylum. Here he found his métier. The Indian project was abandoned, and he entered on the work which was to absorb his energies throughout a long and busy life—the study of the physiology and the pathology of mind.

In 1862, following short terms of service at Wakefield Asylum and the Manchester Royal Lunatic Asylum, he returned to London as resident physician at a private mental home. Shortly afterwards he became editor of *The Journal of Mental Science*—a post he held for six years. In 1864 he

* The following information has been drawn chiefly from articles by Sir George H. Savage and by Dr. F. W. Mott, F.R.S., in *The Journal of Mental Science*, April, 1918.

was appointed physician to the West London Hospital, and from 1869 to 1879 was Professor of Medical Jurisprudence at University College. His retirement took place in 1903 and his death in January, 1918.

Dr. Maudsley's published works included *The Physiology of Mind* (1867), *The Pathology of Mind* (1867), *Body and Mind* (1870) and *Natural Causes and Supernatural Seemings* (1886). He was also a voluminous writer of articles and reviews, and he lectured frequently under the auspices of the London Sunday Lecture Society. While still in the early twenties he showed himself an original and deep thinker. His first essays in *The Journal of Medical Science*, written when he was only twenty-three, led the editor, Dr. Bucknill, to call him "the young philosopher." In this connection it is significant that Maudsley's grandfather was known among his friends as "the old philosopher," on account of his sardonic sayings. The grandson apparently had his full share of the ancestral trait since, according to Sir George H. Savage, who followed him as editor of *The Journal of Mental Science*, to many people Dr. Maudsley appeared "cynical and rather unfriendly" and seemed to prefer solitude and contemplations to social life.

His cynicism and aloofness, however, co-existed with profound human sympathy. From his first contact with the problems of mental disease he held, and expressed in his characteristically uncompromising fashion, strong feelings about the treatment of the insane. His objections to the exercise of undue control over mental patients were carried to the point of condemning forcible feeding save in the most exceptional cases. A few years after his retirement he offered to the London County Council the sum of £30,000 to build a hospital for the early treatment of acute mental cases. His object (eventually realised in the Maudsley Hospital, Denmark Hill) was threefold : to obviate the necessity for sending such cases to the county asylums, to aid research, and to provide valuable training for students of mental diseases.

Dr. Maudsley's approach to mental and other problems was consistently scientific. In his first article contributed to *The Journal of Mental Science* he struck the keynote of his reasoning :—

Science cannot be possibly rejected, and must be accepted. It must be regarded as affording data on which to found the investigation of the real and the spiritual, or by whatever name it is called. The enlightened mind conquers Nature by obeying her. Conscious soul may forget; unconscious soul does not. Of all vanities metaphysics is the vanity of vanities, and the study thereof is vexation of spirit.

The same principle was restated in a volume of essays, *Religion and Realities*, compiled shortly before his death: "Let man apply himself, with all reverence, to Nature, as much of knowable Nature as he can ever know." It was applied, consistently and with striking effect, to the fundamental concepts of religion in *Natural Causes and Supernatural Seemings*—a book which reveals the psychological processes by which man arrived at the beliefs so readily and so widely attributed to mystical sources. The issue implied in the title confronts each generation on reaching intellectual maturity, and Dr. Maudsley's treatment of it, his cool objective exposure of the mental roots of all forms of obscurantism, is as vital to-day as when it was first undertaken.

The present edition is an abridgment of the revised edition published in 1896. Care has been taken, in reducing the original text within the limits of the Thinker's Library, to retain the essential message unimpaired; the omissions relate mainly to supplementary examples of mysticism and superstition and to ancillary discussions.

CONTENTS

PAGE

THE ARGUMENT I

PART I

COMMON FALLACIES OF THE SOUND MIND

CHAP.

I. THE NATURAL DEFECTS AND ERRORS OF OBSERVATION AND REASONING . . 5

II. THE NATURAL DEFECTS AND ERRORS OF OBSERVATION AND REASONING—*continued* 26

III. IMAGINATION : ITS NATURE AND FUNCTION 44

IV. IMAGINATION : ITS ILLUSIONS . . . 51

V. IMAGINATION : ITS PHYSICAL BASIS . . 62

PART II

UNSOUND MENTAL ACTION

I. MENTAL MALFORMITIES 79

II. HALLUCINATIONS AND ILLUSIONS . . 85

III. HALLUCINATIONS AND ILLUSIONS—*continued* 96

IV. MANIA AND DELUSION 109

V. NATURAL AND SUPERNATURAL RELIGION . 118

PART III

THEOPNEUSTICISM : THE ATTAINMENT OF SUPERNATURAL KNOWLEDGE BY DIVINE INSPIRATION

SECTION

I. ECSTATIC INTUITION 122

II. ECSTASY OF FEELING 125

III. INTUITION OF THE HEART . . . 130

IV. THE PHYSICAL BASIS OF ECSTATIC INTUITION 135

V. THEOLOGICAL ILLUMINATION . . . 140

VI. THEOLOGY AND METAPHYSICS . . . 146

THE ARGUMENT

MANY and divers are the notions that have been conceived of the supernatural by different peoples in different ages and places of the earth. From the beginnings of thought on it, when Nature, having reached the stage of self-conscious reflection in man, began to wonder and ask about the whence, why, and whither of its way in the universe, there has been a succession of births and deaths of supernatural beings, of various forms and natures, to meddle in human affairs. Suited to the human conditions in which they were born and lived, they pined and died, one after another, when the changing conditions of thought were no longer fitted to sustain and maintain them. Extinct gods are pretty nigh as plentiful in history as extinct volcanoes on earth. The rule being that those of one age and people were instinctively and deadly hostile to those of another age and people, it came to pass that the weaker gods of weak nations were worsted in the struggle for existence by the stronger gods of strong nations, and eventually exterminated; sometimes, before extinction, suffering a degradation of rank into evil demons, to whom a few belated followers—faithful though few and year by year fewer, themselves perhaps subdued into slavery —continued to pay stealthy worship by secret rites in secret places. For as the conquerors made slaves of the conquered, so they made demons of their deities, stigmatizing the worship of them as base and malignant superstition.

An impartial and critical survey of these sequent travails of human transition might provoke the natural enquiry, Is there any supernatural at all? and, if so, the further enquiry, Has mankind any means of access to it?

Supernatural existence in the sense of something beyond the natural with which human faculties, being the limited and shallow things they are, can come into relation is a manifest necessity of sane human thought. As the senses are only so many narrow chinks of experience between two unknown infinities, the infinitely great and the infinitely small, the knowledge which comes through them, necessarily informed by them, is at best but gleams of light in a surrounding darkness. It would not be light at all to any creature not similarly constituted. Even within the narrow range of sense-experience there is good reason to believe that man's senses cannot reveal to him all which the sensibilities of lower creatures in the animal scale reveal to them.

The very structure of a minute insect, if we well consider it, is effect and proof of more subtle sensibilities and reactions. Think of the power and purpose concentrated in its minute nervous machinery. Man can hardly ever admire enough such mighty works of his inventive skill as the locomotive and the steamship, yet a little fly incorporates in its structure a more wonderful machinery by which it keeps pace with the locomotive in speed, and does more powerful and more intelligent work in proportion to its bulk. And what might the spider, the gossamer threads of whose exquisite web look almost as if woven of a sunbeam or a zephyr, think of the gross machinery which he needs in order to weave his comparatively coarse fabrics? If it be said that an all-powerful Artificer has designed and framed the exquisite structures, it is still a duty—imperative, though unheeded—to take note and thought of the fact that nature only does explicitly by human art through the human nervous system, in a comparatively coarse and clumsy way, what it has done before and is doing elsewhere now in a finer and more perfect way by insect's art through the insect's nervous system.

It is a conceit of man's egotism that his universe

is the measure of every other creature's universe. For aught he knows, the universe, as it is within his experience, may be unlike the universe as it is within other living experience, and no more like the universe outside his experience, which he cannot think, than the universe of a mite is like his universe. To the infinitely little and great he is alike insensible.

Supernatural existence, mighty or minute, in the sense of existence beyond the reach of human faculties may not be denied. But the term is used in quite different sense to mean, not that which is unknown and cannot be known, but a known supernatural world peopled by supernatural beings—gods and devils, good and evil spirits, the blessed souls of good men made perfect, and the damned souls of bad men left imperfect, with whom communication can be made by supernatural ways. Has man then ever had, and has he even now, any such means of knowing the beings and events of such a world, however peopled, beyond the natural world? If he has not, how is it that so many people in so many times and places have believed that they had? If he has, how is it that there has been no agreement between the supernaturally inspired accounts given of its beings and doings, but that the stories have been as divers as the peoples, sometimes as gross and barbarous?

Surveying the matter calmly from a purely scientific point of view, two things are obvious : first, that those who say that nothing can be known of the supernatural ought to go to work to show how it has come to pass that so much has been known or misknown of it—to account as natural events for the many positive and precise beliefs concerning it; secondly, that those who profess to know what goes on in the supernatural world are bound to show how that knowledge has been obtained, to test and prove its authenticity, and to demonstrate finally and conclusively which of the different and opposed revelations is the true one. The enquiry, a purely scientific one, ought to be begun and prosecuted frankly in a candid spirit, entirely free from all prepossession by any theory of the supernatural ; for to begin with a bias of that kind is infallibly to prejudge the problem and to vitiate the enquiry from the outset.

In pursuit of this much-needed enquiry, How it has come to pass that men have been able to think so many things about that which lies beyond the reach of thought?, I propose to set forth the chief causes of error in thinking which might lead, and have largely led, to wrong theories of the supernatural, classifying them under three headings :—

I. Those which belong to the natural operations of mind and may be included in two principal classes, namely,

> 1. The natural defects and errors of observation and reasoning,
> 2. The prolific activity of imagination.

II. Those which belong to the operations of unsound mind and fall naturally under the two headings of

> 1. Hallucinations and illusions,
> 2. Mania and delusions.

III. Those which belong to the extraordinary workings of mind rapt in ecstasies or transports of feeling and imagination, and are thought to mark intuition raised to its highest power of illumination ; a state of mind which, being deemed more than ordinarily mental, is styled *spiritual*.

PART I

COMMON FALLACIES OF THE SOUND MIND

CHAPTER I

THE NATURAL DEFECTS AND ERRORS OF OBSERVATION AND REASONING

§ *Uniformities of Experience.*

WERE a simple-minded rustic asked how he is sure that from one kind of seed, when put into the ground, will spring up one kind of plant, and from another kind of seed another kind of plant, he might answer, if he deigned to answer at all, that any fool who knows one seed from another knows that much. It would be a rude but forcible statement of the truth that even a fool fails not to notice so common and constant a succession of events. In like manner, were the astronomer asked how it is that he can foretell the events of the heavens at such immense distances of space and time, he might say, if not prompted by scientific vanity to magnify and make a mystery of his calling, that every astronomer who knows his business can do it, and cannot help doing it, as well as he can. In either case the reasoned inference rests upon uniformity of experience, on the conviction that what has been is that which shall be in the order of nature, and in neither case has it any authority other than experience : not individual experience alone, it may be, but the slowly gained and capitalized experience of the race embodied now in the general statement of the uniform experience—that is, in the so-called law of nature.

So long as the order of nature is what it is, so long

must men, constituted as they are, look for co-
existences and sequences to be in time to come as they
have been in time past. So long, too, will they be
prone, in consequence of faulty observation and hasty
inference, to make mistakes by supposing connections
of things which are common but not constant,
perhaps occasional only, to be invariable and necessary
—by concluding casual to be causal events. The
more stupid the individual the less evidence does he
then need for his conclusion, the more sure he is of
it, the blinder is he to its disproof, the more foolish
are the mistakes which he makes. If he has once
broken a mirror, or spilt salt on the table-cloth, or
sat down to dinner in a company of thirteen, when
some misfortune followed, he goes on believing to the
end of his life that he cannot break a mirror, or spill
salt on the table-cloth, or sit down thirteen to dinner,
without bringing inevitable ill luck. He may be
vastly comforted if, after the untoward event, he can
think to break the spell of the ill omen by immediately
invoking, to cancel it, another omen, equally absurd,
which is reputed to be of auspicious import.

It is hard to *conceive*, harder still to *believe*, a contradiction of uniform experience. If two things or events
always go along together they are inevitably thought of
together, and thereupon believed to be bound together
by an inviolate tie, not in the mind only, but in the
nature of things. In mind it could not be otherwise.
So, too, might it be in nature were the human mind
commensurate with the universe and all its workings
in mass and molecule, if, being omnisensible and
omniscient, its uniform were universal experience;
but as that is not so, nor ever likely to be so, knowledge being limited to a narrow chink of light between
two infinities of darkness and necessarily at best as
shallow as narrow, the mental tie may or may not
mean a tie of things. Occasions of error present
themselves at every turn. A wider experience and
larger reason may prove the apparently invariable
to be really a variable association. All swans were

believed to be white until a black swan was seen for the first time in Australia; "swan" and whiteness being two notions that went together inseparably. The right use of a contradictory instance in reasoning is to correct the erroneous generalization by proving that it is not really general, and thereby to bring the order of thought into agreement with the order of nature.

But the contradictory experience fails often to refute the wrong conclusion. That is the pregnant fault which gives birth to frequent fallacy of reasoning. Once the opinion is universally accepted, handed down by tradition, ingrained in habit of thought, it is so incorporate in the mental nature as to be invested with an authority greater than experience has given or could ever give; it acquires a kind of sacred sanction which it is thought impious to question. Like the instinct of the animal, fashioned and fixed through the ages, it is a very principle of the mental structure. Reverenced rightly at first for its use as a necessary bond of social continuity and unity, it is over-reverenced in the end as a religion, and invested with the privilege of sanctuary from criticism; then it survives in spite of contradictory experience, is literally a superstition.

Another reason which no doubt helps to prevent the refuting contradiction from cancelling the wrong conclusion is the common dictum, so commonly misunderstood, that the exception proves the rule. When the exception proves the rule it is not in the sense of justifying and establishing it, but in the sense of probing and testing it, and thus, when the exception is a true one, of disproving it : not a case of proving a wrong theory of uniformity by the exception, but of disproving it by the probing instance which the exception is. To a true generalization it is impossible there should be a true exception. How could it be general if there were? The element of prudent truth in the popular saying, if we consider it well, is a tacit acknowledgment of the fallibility of human

generalizations and an implied caution not to base
rules of practice too absolutely on them in human
affairs.

Why is human nature hostile to new thought and
action? Because it is new, and, being new, agrees
not with the old. How can the old mental nature
like and welcome that which disagrees with and,
therefore, is a dislike to it? In face of the novel
experience which it is unable to apprehend and deal
with definitely, mind is perplexed and powerless in
the first instance, for the impression is devoid of
any connections with its existing ideas; it cannot help
staggering for a while in giddy confusion. There
is no peace then until either the new thing be ignored
or a new mental adjustment to it be organized.

Belief is notoriously so much a custom of nature,
and nothing more, in the great majority of men that
they can no more think a new belief befitting new
circumstances, or correct an old belief not fitting
them, than they can speak a foreign language of
which they know nothing. That is not entirely an
evil on earth; organically fashioned machines which
have to do their mechanical work in the world, they
are often better instruments for their humble functions
than they would be if they were endowed with less
servility and more plasticity of mind. The habit
of mind no doubt makes for the repose of the individual and the stability of a people; a coarse
mental machinery is suited to its environment
and works fitly in it; but the habit is none the less
fatal to mental progress, which takes place only by
putting off old beliefs when they have been found
wanting, and putting on new beliefs in conformity
with new observation and reflection. A good effect
of wide experience of men and things, and of a wise
and large mental culture, is to emancipate the mind
from the bondage of custom and to open the way to
impressions which may modify, perhaps overthrow,
old conceptions; then when the new thing presents
itself it is not impatiently rejected, nor relegated hastily

to a category which fits it not, but is closely heeded, quietly reflected on, and duly sorted or assimilated.

§ *Sanctification of Error as Superstition.*

A great cause, then, of ordinary errors of thought, and of ordinary errors that have obtained extraordinary sanctity as superstitions, is an unfounded belief in instances of uniformity which are not really such, and the survival or persistence of such errors in beliefs and customs after they are or ought to be discredited by observation. The things which, when they went together before, were followed by good luck, will, when they go together again, bring good luck after them, and a day on which a misfortune has befallen becomes an unlucky day. The repugnance is still strong, and in former days there was a religious prohibition against commencing important business on the unlucky day. In reality there may be no more connection between the two events than there is between an eclipse of the sun and the birth of a red-haired child which chances to take place during it, or between the flaming of a comet in the heavens and the career of a great conqueror or a great criminal who is born under that aspect of them. More than eighteen hundred years have passed since Ovid referred to the vulgar objection of the Romans to marriages in May, the probable reason of the aversion being that the funeral rites of the Lemuralia were celebrated in that month; but the superstition is still not extinct, for marriages in May are thought by many to be unlucky now. How vivid and piercing a ray of light does the fact throw into the persistence, for good or ill, of past, be it never so remote, in present human thought and feeling !

The priests of ancient Rome, making their profit out of this omen-seeking habit of mind, as the medicine-men of savage tribes do still, sought and, seeking, found in the entrails of the animals offered up as sacrifices to the gods the signs propitious or unpropitious to the enterprise about to be undertaken; and the derivation of omens from the flights of birds was developed into an elaborate science, feeble survivals of which are found in the superstitions that still linger in remote country villages as to the good or ill luck portended by flights of magpies. How little truth of observation was at the bottom of omens of the kind, widespread and hallowed as they were among all sorts of people in all quarters of the earth, is shown clearly by the fact that the same event which was an omen of ill luck in one nation might be an omen of good fortune in another nation, and that the same bird might presage good or bad fortune according as it was to the right or the left of the person who chanced to see it.

When prayers were made daily to saints in Christendom, with a deeper sense of reality and a more vital belief in their efficacy than exists now, or than a modern nature can feel in the modern atmosphere of thought, one saint was invoked as specially propitious to one person or one class of persons, and another saint to another person or another class of persons; whence it did not fail sometimes to happen that the saint who was the patron of one was hostile to another when the interests of the two conflicted. Having prayed once to a particular saint and received what he prayed for, the suppliant was persuaded that he got it in consequence of his prayer, and ever afterwards invoked that saint with heart of good hope, notwithstanding that on a hundred other occasions he did not get what he prayed for. In some Roman Catholic churches at the present day the walls inside are covered with the votive tablets of those who, having prayed to the Virgin or to a favourite saint for the recovery of a mother, child, sister, brother, father, or lover from sickness, have thus recorded their gratitude for the favourable answer which the event has been. And so in English churches still, when the country is suffering damage from the long continuance of wet weather, so that the harvest cannot be gathered in, and the farmer looks round him in despair at the rain which continues to fall, special prayer is made solemnly to Almighty God, that He may turn from the people those evils which they for their sins have most righteously deserved, by sending fine weather. If fine weather comes at length after the long spell of wet weather, it is a manifest and merciful answer to prayer; if not, the credit of prayer nowise suffers by its ill success on the occasion.

§ *Fallacies of Coincidence in Reasoning.*

It might naturally be thought that people of all countries in all ages would not have offered sacrifices and supplications to their gods had not the events often answered the expectations of those who were at the cost and pains of offering them. Propitiatory hecatombs of slain creatures, human and animal, offered up in countless numbers on countless altars in all parts of the world—are they not proof of the existence of gods who have inclined their ears to hear the urgent prayers of mankind? Not so; since the many gods that were thus invoked and propitiated with costly rites and ceremonies amid the reverential awe of their adoring worshippers are now confessed to have had no existence outside human imagination, and not ever therefore to have answered the prayers they were believed to answer at the time. Their present interest is as extinct beliefs, not as extinct beings.

Why, then, were they thought to answer prayers? In the main, perhaps, for a reason which still works strongly as a cause of error in reasoning—namely, the well-known tendency of the mind, so much insisted on by Bacon, to be impressed vividly by agreeing instances and to remember them, while overlooking and forgetting the opposing instances. But for it the prodigies and prophecies which have heralded the ruins of great states and great persons, as well as such comfortable opinions as that "murder will out," that "truth will prevail," and the like, would have long since lost their credit. It is obvious that those who see proof of the power and goodwill of the gods when they look round on the numerous votive tablets which are so many records of their benevolent interpositions in human affairs, do not think or care to ask themselves where are the votive tablets of the vastly greater number of persons who received no answers to their prayers?

So it was with the astrologers of old, who, noting the fortunes of persons born when a particular constellation was in the ascendant, professed to predict the fortunes of those born under the same celestial auspices, although one of two persons born at the same instant might become a prince and the other a beggar, and were never a whit shaken in their pretensions and authority by the multitude of their failures. So it is with the fortune-teller of to-day, who imposes on the credulity of the ignorant by the authority of some remarkable instance or instances in which his prediction was verified by the event. So in a signal manner has it been with the observation and use of dreams; for it has not only been a common saying that dreams come true, but the opposite saying that dreams go by contraries has also had its vogue. Always the remembrances of the hits stand out vividly, while the misses fade into oblivion.

Were a curious collection made of all the various omens that have been in repute among different nations and in different times, in order to find out whether the greater number of them were believed to portend good fortune or misfortune, without doubt the ill omens would preponderate largely over the good omens, just as the demons and evil spirits have preponderated over the benevolent fairies and the good spirits. The obvious reason is that the omens foreboding ill have obtained more credit because of their more frequent fulfilment, misfortunes and misery being more common in the world than good fortune and blessings, however optimists may pretend differently. Friday still has a bad pre-eminence as an unlucky day, not because it is really more unlucky than another day, but because any day of the week on which attentive note was taken, through a long succession of experiences, of the events happening on it would have a pre-ponderance of ills; a proof of this being that, in the opinion of some persons, Monday is an unlucky day on which to begin a new enterprise. Omens of good fortune, being more often discredited by the event, would be limited to comparatively rare occurrences and sequences.

Presentiments, omens, auguries, telepathic chimings of distant thought, monitory dreams, and like vague adumbrations of mysterious and ineffable relations between men and things, which mystical minds admire with awe as symbols of truth too deep for reach of definite intellectual apprehension, will all be found, when critically examined, to owe their credit in the main, if not entirely, to crude observation and bad reasoning. At any rate, the indistinct and shadowy relations which such minds perceive, or feel vaguely rather than perceive, are not necessarily proofs of superfine insight into things; they certainly often betray the visionary vagrancy of the indolent and self-indulgent mind which, shirking the labour of clear and precise thinking, delights to drift in a vagabondage of misty feeling and shadowy thought. The mystical intimations are not then sublime because they are obscure; they are obscure because, phantom-like, they love the twilight and shrink from facing the light of thought.

It is not to be denied that an undefined foreboding of evil, a deep and tragical presentiment, sometimes in a person's life goes before a calamity which was not foreseen, not even dimly anticipated. Such dark premonition, when fulfilled by the event, is a circumstance well suited to beget the opinion of a supernatural intimation. The cases in which it occurs are, I think, of two classes : (*a*) before the outset of some severe bodily illness like fever which perhaps ends fatally; (*b*) before the explosion of some brooding catastrophe in the individual's affairs or social relations.

In the first case a supernatural explanation is not needed, since a brooding disease, especially when it has what is known medically as its period of incubation, may be forefelt in the bodily economy, which it threatens, as a vague, sad foreboding, before it is so far developed as to exhibit its proper form and symptoms and to be perceived. The language of feeling goes before the language of thought in the order of human development, and has a deeper significance in the nature of mental function. Peradventure the prophetic feeling of evil to come takes form in the person's dreams of a particular disease before the lurking disease in him shows itself, as it subsequently does; and it may certainly translate itself in the instinctive certitude of a sick man that he will die, though he is only at the beginning of an illness the symptoms of which, on the face of them, warrant not the expressed despair. Here, as elsewhere, if not everywhere else, the notion of a supernatural agency springs from the ignorance of natural causes.

Nor do the facts in the second class of cases, when they are examined closely, lie outside the bounds of a natural explanation. To fore*feel* vaguely is no less natural than to fore*see* clearly; it only seems more mysterious because the intimations of feeling have not yet been studied and defined like the language of thought; have not, in fact, been interpreted methodically at all.

However, when pleasing conjecture has had its way in the interpretation of these mysterious phenomena, sober reflection must needs allow the greatest weight to the vulgar and stubborn fallacy of concluding from agreeing without regard to opposing instances. It is a joy to the mind to mark the hits, it is a strain to it to mark the misses. If anybody chances to think of a friend at the Antipodes about the time when he hears later to his surprise that his friend died (and in subsequent narration the uncertain time is pretty sure to become the exact moment), or feels unaccountably sad just before an unforeseen misfortune befalls, he is vividly impressed by, and pleased to tell, the awe-striking story of the singular coincidence; but he takes no note of the many instances when he unexpectedly thought of a friend who did not die at that exact moment or at all, nor of the many times when he felt unaccountably sad without the sequel of a great misfortune.

That there are many more things in heaven and earth than philosophy can spell out or so much as dream of, and mysterious feelings in man which come either as pulses from the far-reaching depths of humanity within him, or are caused by unknown conditions of nature without him, may readily be admitted. But it is to go a long way beyond the warrant of observation and reason to accept off-hand the stories of spiritual apparitions and mysterious sympathies which have had, and still have, a strong hold on popular credence—stories whose hot attestation blazons the need of their confirmation. For example : the apparition of a person at the moment of his death, in his form and habit as he lived, to a friend a thousand miles away; the dream of someone's place and time and mode of death at the exact time and place, and in the exact way it took place; the communication of a thought or feeling between two persons who are in different rooms of the same house or in different houses miles apart; and why not add the more vulgar instance (which rests, after all, on a wider basis of experience) of the tingling of a person's ear when somebody is somewhere talking about him? Although these and like stories are positively vouched for by zealous observers whose credibility lacks nothing except what it suffers from the entire lack in them of a capacity to observe, they are believed rather because they are wished than because they are proved to be true; they might be expected therefore still to hold their ground stoutly in faith were they disproved by the positive evidence of facts.

When two neurotic persons, eager to make discoveries in psychical research, go to work to test diligently by experiment whether the one, when he mounts to the attic, can respond instantly by telepathic sympathy of thought to the thought which the other conceives in the kitchen, having carefully prearranged the conditions of the experiment so as to avoid any collusion except the unconscious subtle collusion of their like-structured minds, it would perhaps be strange, human nature being what it is, if the two did not echo. One knows not indeed which to admire most—the simple zeal for the truth, or the zealous simplicity with which two colluding natures go about conscientiously to prevent collusion.

The experiment so conducted is pathetically absurd. For it is not they who ought to conduct it —it is they who require to be controlled as factors in the conducted experiment; and that should be done by a cool and competent outside observer, unbiased and critical, who regulates strictly all the proper conditions and tests. The pity of it in such case notably is that the presence of a sceptical mind is hostile to the conduction of the telepathic sympathy, or to the spiritual manifestation, which so resents the irreverent tests that the expected event does not then come off; like the miracle, it requires an ambient medium of believing minds—it fails to show itself in the unfit medium of unbelievers because of their unbelief.

Now an event which cannot tolerate the searching conditions alone sufficient to test it scientifically, but claims a privilege of sanctuary from the criticism of reason, belongs logically to the domain of that kind of faith which is proud to exult over reason.

§ *Fallacies of Coincidence in Observation.*

The proneness of the mind to respond to agreeing and to overlook differing or opposing instances, out of which so many errors of thought have sprung, is not manifest in reasoning from facts only, it works equally in the observation or perception of the facts themselves: it is the tendency which so often vitiates direct observation of that which lies plain to sense were sense only applied plainly to it. A wrong idea or image of the fact, suggested by some like features of it, precludes perception of the real fact. How easy is it to make mistakes as to the identities of persons, and how often it happens that a witness, or one witness after another, swears positively in a court of justice to the identity of a person who is not only not the person he is sworn to be, but perhaps is not much like him. Nothing can be more positive than the assurance with which the mistaken evidence is given on such occasion, nothing more inexcusable as an example of observation, nothing more instructive as an illustration of a common fallacy of observation.

As in reasoning, so in perception, the tendency to generalize is stronger than the tendency to discriminate. What happens is that the striking likeness of one or two features excites the notion of a certain person in the observer's mind, and that the mental image thus raised so usurps his attention that he has no eyes for the manifest and manifold differences in the real object. Attention, fascinated by the like, cannot attend to the unlike.

Were any one to mark and mind that which he really sees and hears in the course of a day, he might be not a little surprised to discover how small a part of what he thinks he sees and hears he does actually see and hear, and how often he thinks he sees and hears much that he never sees and hears at all. Passing glimpses suggest objects, as passing sounds do words, which in most cases, no doubt, are the proper objects and words, but by no means always so; for, if careful attention be given on each occasion to the supposed perception, and it be pursued home to actual verification, it will be found in not a few instances that the object seen or the word heard was not really what it was thought to be, in some instances perhaps not even the object or word at all. The healthiest mind, in the course of its daily experiences, has many passing illusions or hallucinations of that sort, which it does not stay to test and correct, because they are mere transient incidents, of no concern to its immediate purpose; as in like manner, when not seriously occupied, it has the strangest vagaries of thought and fancy that come and go unheeded. Every one knows that the mind plays many tricks in sleep, but few persons realize, until they observe themselves closely and reflect on what they observe, how many like tricks it plays habitually in waking life. Let loose from the restraining hold of its habits of experience, it gambols almost as riotously as in dreams.

Let any one be put in face of some new fact or relation which he is required to observe for the first time, or of a new feature of an old fact or relation, he comes to it necessarily with a mind preoccupied with notions of facts or relations which he has observed formerly and which do not fit it, and devoid of notions which fit it. How, then, can he truly mind it? It is impossible that he can observe it rightly in the first instance, not having the suitable interpretation-notions—no cerebral reflexes fitted to perform it. At the same time, he could not mind the fact at all, any more than he could know an acquaintance, if he had not the prepossession of some related notion. The present and future cannot be thought by any-body but in terms of the past; for thought is instructed by informed experience, and cannot go beyond it until it has been reinformed—reconstructed, that is—by new experience: the past is the indispensable basis of any knowledge of the present, and of any prediction or expectation with regard to the future.

To every one a *thing* is what he *thinks* it—in effect, a *think*; and to think a new thing he must first use the old thought. How can he do otherwise before new experience enables him to organize a new *think*? The old *thing* or *think* represents object *plus* subject; the new thing, therefore, is no thing to him until it is asselfed in a think, for until then it is object *minus* subject. The bent of the mind so preoccupied is, first of all, to resist the intrusion of the new notion with silent stubbornness, since there is no place for it; afterwards, when the passive barrier is forced, with angry prejudice, passion coming to the aid of the resistance, since it is a shock to the organized tracks of thought; and, last of all, when the intruder has gained admission, to mould it into the shapes of its own notions as much as possible, so forming it to its liking as, perhaps, to deform it.

For a like reason it is that discoveries in science and inventions in the arts have a long and tedious gestation, although they seem most simple and easy when they are brought forth to light. So obvious, once made, that the wonder is they were overlooked for a day, yet overlooked through so many generations that the wonder is they were made at last. Naturally they were inconceivable before they were conceived, and as naturally they are easily conceivable when once they have been conceived. In divining what may be one cannot but proceed from the basis of what has been and what is, and so construct the new in forms of the old. The new conception starts not out of the head, Minerva-like, complete in itself and ready to undergo the full test of experiment; it is reached tentatively and by degrees, by modifications of old notions through impressions made by altered facts and relations, much of the modifying impression being unconscious in the first instance. The increments of experience silently saturate the mind until they crystallize consciously into a new conception of things; just as if, after much patient brooding over the subject, a nervous circuit of discovery, electric-like, were suddenly closed. Then the last man who expounds and proves gets the credit of the discovery because he gives the final exposition; the gradual maturing in silent gestation, making no show, for the most part passes unheeded.

Accidents are oftentimes the happy occasions of inventions, as observations of animals have been from time to time, because, presenting things to the mind under new aspects and in new relations, they startle thought out of its deep grooves of habit and so provoke new adjustments and reflections. No doubt there is often as much new instruction to be had out of old and common things, were they only observed carefully and curiously with open sense and free mind, as can be obtained from the most ingenious experiments to devise new combinations of things; but the difficulty is to break the thrall of unheeding habit and to stir attention to what one is not used to heed. So it becomes necessary to go about to make new experiments, or to await the happy thought-kindling accident, in order to discover that which a familiar instance lying close at hand might teach plainly if duly minded. Why is this thing so? Why is this thing not truly so?—these are two questions which, if clearly put and rigorously answered in regard to many common experiences, might often reveal new and unsuspected truth.

§ *Laws of Assimilation and Discrimination.*

In the strong impression made on the mind by coincidences and resemblances, whereby it happens that dissidences and differences are so easily overlooked and neglected both in observation and reasoning, we have then at bottom an instance of the law of mental assimilation. Like takes to itself like as that which, agreeing with it, it naturally likes to do; and inasmuch as, while doing that, it occupies the attention, engrossing the consciousness, the contradictory instance or difference is inevitably left much or entirely in the dark. To attend is literally to tend to, and one attention, when it is so strung as to be tension, physically excludes another attention.

The order of notions in the best mind and in the best achievements of the best minds, falls infinitely short of reflecting the order of things in nature, either in exactness or in completeness, since it consists of multitudinous partial relations and groups of relations, incomplete, fragmentary, and superficial; and that always within a very limited range compared with the limitless range of inaccessible phenomena. It is the business of observation to make the correspondence more exact, more connected, more complete within its range, and, if so be, to extend the range; a work which must in the nature of things always be gradual, since such fuller knowledge, entailing new or changed ideas, imports a demand upon the mental organization to put in function, if not to develop, new lines of organic structure.

This organization of new cerebral reflexes it cannot do at all, except under these conditions—that it retain its plastic energy, and that it takes the time necessary to do it.

Compare in this relation an old man with a child: both hold confidently to the associations of ideas which experience has ingrafted in them; but while the old man, whose mental tissues are dull and stiff with the rigidity of age, is unable easily or at all to relinquish them, and little curious or able to assimilate new ideas and to make adjustments to new circumstances, the child, though quite as strongly dominated by the few notional associations which it has—and in the nature of things cannot conceive otherwise until it is exposed to new experiences—is full of eager curiosity, quickly impressionable by new facts, aptly plastic in thought, feeling, and conduct to new surroundings. When the brain, by reason of a natural simplicity of constitution in the low savage and in the animal, or of congenital defect in the imbecile, is without the nervous substrata necessary to subserve new developments of function, then it is impossible to ingraft the finer and more complex associations of ideas, and almost impossible to dissociate the few simple and common ones which the circumstances of life have occasioned. The mental organization, being simple and general, is little modifiable; for the more complex and special the more modifiable it is.

How should the savage separate in thought two events that have always gone together in his experience? It would be as easy for him to separate two movements which he had never in his life performed separately. How can he learn a new thought, the organic basis of which, being laid only by the conquests of culture through many generations, his simple brain is destitute of? Charms and prayers, auguries and omens, oracles, ordeals, exorcisms, incantations, and divinations are the natural resort and refuge, as they are the exponents, of active imagination co-operating with defective observation and little-developed understanding. Man must have something definite in the way of belief, must believe something, in order to act at all; acting, then, in relation to a vast and mysterious universe of which he knows next to nothing, he is compelled to fashion for himself forms or species of it, however provisional, as fixed stays or supports. Believing in sorcery, he imagines a sorcerer, and, striving to get rid of him, institutes trial by ordeal, in order to detect the hidden worker of mysterious evil; thus he establishes an agency in relation to which at all events he can act definitely, and gains some sense of security from unknown dangers. In the inapprehensible immensity he cannot choose but make a little enclosure of some sort in which to fence himself.

§ *The Favourable Conditions of Superstition.*

It is obvious that the tendency of mind to give undue weight to the according event, and no heed to the events which do not answer desire or expectation—so fruitful a cause of errors of observation and reasoning—has been a great, if not the main, cause of the authority and credit which so many superstitions have enjoyed. Has it not notably been just where observation and reasoning were difficult or impossible that superstitions have sprung up and flourished? It is in proportion as observation and reasoning have become more proficient that superstitions have dwindled and died. Is there a single person living now who believes that Baal ever answered a single prayer of the devout Canaanite? Or that Jupiter ever inclined his ear to hear the supplication of a pious Roman? Or that the Mexican was any the better for the human sacrifices which he solemnly offered to Uitzilopochtli? Not one is left now to do the dead gods reverence. But it would have gone hard with him who, living when these gods ruled in human faith, had made a denial of their power and good or ill will. They were faiths which, being without foundation in reason, were destined inevitably to wane and vanish before the brighter light of better sense and reason.

The history of medicine, like the history of religion, is full of examples of fallacious observations and of superstitious theories; and for the same reason—namely, the extreme difficulties of observation and the strong propensity to supernatural beliefs where mystery and fear prevail. The human organism is the most intricate and complex structure in the world; a fabric of such nice and implicated correlations of parts and functions that the more its mechanism is known the more the wonder grows that it ever keeps in working order so well and so long as it does; and it is in infinitely subtle and complex relations with a variety of external influences, physical and social.

B

The exact causes of its disorders and the exact means of putting them right are inevitably, therefore, the most difficult and complex study in the world, and being so they yield large scope for fallacies of observation and inference. Many therefore, were the false theories of diseases, and many the monstrous remedies for them which enjoyed immense reputation for a season, to be abandoned ultimately as useless or pernicious.

§ *Fallacies of Collusion.*

The fallacy of observation and reasoning by which a nation was deluded into the flattering belief of its directly intervening god in special answer to prayer must have worked powerfully to sustain and strengthen the belief, which, without it, could hardly have taken such frequent root and flourished so strongly as history proves it to have done. But, though a main, this fallacy of coincidence was not the entire cause of the credit of superstitions of the kind. In cases of signal accord betwen the omen or prayer and its fulfilment, where a chance-coincidence was so improbable as practically to exclude the notion of it, and where, therefore, the claim of a causal relation might well seem undeniable, no proper account was taken of the possibility of collusion.

Now, this collusion might take place not only between persons concerned, whose interest it was to make the experiment a success, and who, consciously or unconsciously, conspired together for that purpose, as priests, rulers, omen-mongers, workers of magic, and the like dupers of mankind have often done, but might be a self-connivance. There have always been individuals more wise than the multitude, who, making the natural use of their superior sagacity to gain advantages for themselves, have fooled it for their power and profit, and often at the same time for its good—Minos pretending to be advised by Jupiter, Numa retiring to take secret counsel of

Ægeria, and many more like tricks used by the founders
of different religions the better to beguile; and it is
very certain that in this way projects and laws and
institutions obtained an authority and acceptance
which they would not have obtained as the mere
counsels of a wiser individual, and that useful customs
and practices were thus consecrated as religious
ceremonials. That which was believed to be the
direct inspiration of the god, and to be done by
supernatural ways, carried a sanction with it which
it had not as the bare inspiration of human wisdom
effected by natural ways; the omen and prayer were
the mysterious means of obtaining supernatural
countenance for the natural event which the sagacious
mind, seeing farther ahead than the vulgar, had foreseen, or had designed, by working impressively on
vulgar minds, to bring to pass.

Not always was the deception entirely wilful—
sheer fraud; witting and systematic deceit of that
kind is comparatively rare. A subtle collusion with
self, a large measure of secret self-deception, made
the author of the dupery to some extent its victim
also. For he who, having an interest or pleasure
in duping others, lets will loose from moral restraint
and makes a practice of acting the part, grows
inevitably and easily to the habit of its exercise,
and finally dupes himself : deliberate impostor by
art, he becomes an ingrained impostor by second
nature; the sure working of natural law thus avenging
wrong-doing on the nature of the wrong-doer. Note
a familiar example of this process of demoralization
in the ease with which one who begins by telling in
dramatic fashion stories that excite wonder sometimes goes on to exaggerate and embellish and invent
until they become complete romances, and in the end
is not himself sure what is true and what is false
in them. His imagination, like that of the opium-
eater, is so demoralized by habitual over-stimulation
that the imaginary seems more real than the real, and
he loses actual sense of the distinction between them.

CHAPTER II

THE NATURAL DEFECTS AND ERRORS OF OBSERVATION AND REASONING—*continued*.

§ *Causes of Erroneous Observation.*

So many and great errors and evils having flowed from bad observation and reasoning, it is natural to ask how it comes to pass that man observes and reasons so badly when his business is to observe and reason. Because he is a limited being with very limited capacities, while that which he has to observe and reason about is unlimited. Observation being the organic construction of an internal order of mind in conformity with the external order of nature, it is a process of mental organization, to be perfected only by degrees, not an instantaneous mental photography.

I go on now to enquire and consider what are the main causes of imperfect and erroneous observation and to summarize them briefly.

(*a*) The natural limitations or shortcomings of the senses.

Men little reflect how limited is that which sense does or can reveal at the best. Were they to consider well that each sense perceives only its special impressions, and cannot perceive the impressions which affect another sense, they might realize better how very little it is which any sense and all the senses together can tell of the external world.

It is not defect of knowledge alone that has ensued from the shortcomings of sense; the defect has given rise to large and far-reaching positive error of thought as its natural consequence. Who can estimate the power and reach of erroneous belief which had its root in the exploded notion, so firmly held before the magnitude of the heavens was made known, that the earth was the centre of the universe? The geocentric theory of the universe went hand in hand with the anthropocentric theory of man as end and aim of creation. How many wrong notions, fallacious theories, ignorant conceits, have flowed from the crude notion of matter, which, conceiving it as gross and inert, precluded the least conception of the nature and movements of its infinitely minute and active molecules? When it is said that matter cannot possibly think, the meaning of the proposition to one who entertains the vulgar notion only of gross inert matter is widely different from what it is to him who, informed by adequate previous study, can conceive how intensely active and subtle are its molecular energies, and realize how its energies rise in concentration and dignity as it attains to higher and higher complexity of organization.

(b) Next in order to the want of means of observation is the want of opportunities of observation.

It is obvious that he who has not the opportunity is practically as ill placed for forming a sound conclusion as he who has not the means of observing; to want the opportunity is to want the use of means. The miracle takes place promptly when those who witness it are forbidden, either by external hindrance or by the sometimes stronger barrier of internal prohibitive scruple, to make a thorough and searching examination of all the circumstances attending its occurrence. Out of question, Voltaire was quite right when he said that magic words are capable of destroying a whole flock of sheep—if the incantation be accompanied with a sufficient dose of arsenic; and, after the event, there will be no doubt of the miracle in the mind of the awe-stricken observer who has not seen more of the performance than the magic ceremonies. A person may rise from the grave after being buried alive for some days (as the Indian fakir does) when rigorous means are not taken to ensure that he is buried completely; and witnesses will

vouch solemnly that they have seen the thing happen
whose sincerity as witnesses is as unquestionable as
their incompetence as observers. A credible eye-
witness in any such matter is a witness who is not
only qualified by natural aptitude and acquired training to make the special observation, but who possesses
the means, uses all the expedients, and exhausts the
opportunities of investigation. Many miracles have
taken place in times past, as the miraculous lique-
faction of the blood of St. Januarius takes place
regularly once a year still, because the true causes of
the event were not critically looked for in a rightly
sceptical spirit. The difficulty in such cases is not
to prevent adequate observation; the difficulty is to
incite men to it. The event strikes the mind with a
pleasing awe, wonder winning assent; but it is pain
and labour to hold assent in abeyance in order to
make a scrupulous and tedious examination of all the
antecedent and accompanying conditions of its occurrence.

Why does wonder win assent? First, because
wonder, like other emotions, craves for and embraces
gladly that which agrees with and is fitted to nourish
it. Secondly, because man, being in relations of
knowledge with so small a part of nature compared
with the vast extent thereof lying beyond any such
relations, but with which nevertheless he is in relations of being—for the bounds of knowledge are
nowise the bounds of being—feels instinctively that
there are many more things in heaven and earth than
are dreamt of in his philosophy; wherefore his
natural attitude of mind is that of awe-struck humility
and vague dread of unforeseen events. This anxious
mood of trembling expectation is exploited by the
miracle and the miracle-monger, who abuses a childlike humility of faith; intimidated belief, without
any resource of knowledge behind it, being overwhelmed and captured by bold assertion.

Moreover, there are other supporting factors.
First, the number of opportunities in the world for

coincidences is practically infinite; very singular and striking ones, well fitted to make a strong impression of mysterious fatality, are met with from time to time; therefore the imposing authority of these remarkable coincidences operates unconsciously, or is designedly used, to strengthen the opinion and feeling of supernatural agency. Then, again, to discredit a popular religious belief is an offence to the feeling and an imputation on the understanding of the majority; for which reason few persons care to shock the common social sense and to incur the penalties of infidelity by speaking the unwelcome truth outright and openly. So the belief is protected from attack and enjoys the privilege of sanctuary from criticism.

(c) A third cause of error of observation may be set down as the want of the habit of observation.

A want of habit is really the want of the capacity of observation; for although one person has a better natural aptitude to observe than another, yet no one can observe well in any province of nature without training by practice, any more than he can ride or dance well without having had practical lessons in riding or dancing. Habit is acquired faculty, function-made structure—structural knowledge or instruction, that is—and thereafter the automatic and easy performance of acts which were performed at first only by conscious labour and perfecting efforts. Exact observation in any special province of science implies the organized power and aptitude to bring, on all necessary occasions, related ideas to bear upon the subject under observation, so as to illume it in all its aspects; and this not with labouring consciousness, but almost automatically. Not only must the related ideas be acquired by observation and reflection, but the habit of applying them, which is power of attention, must be cultivated by practice. Then it is the direct intending of mind to the object, as with a close cerebral reflex grasp, whereby this is apprehended firmly : an internal power which serves and in a sense constrains in all cases, even when the subject is not itself fitted to kindle a particular interest. Withal must be conjoined therewith a habit of strict mental veracity—that is to say, a sincere resolution to see the thing as it is on all occasions, at whatever cost to prejudice or feeling, and not to go a step in assent beyond the measure of the evidence : a heart as well as an eye for the truth. So the best habit of mind for the discovery of truth is formed.

Here a brief consideration may be given to the nature of attention. Psychologists commonly use the term as if they meant by it a separate faculty of mind which it has the power of setting to work or not; and even those among them who think of attention as the voluntary direction of consciousness in a particular channel imply a sort of abstract power of thus turning consciousness at will wherever its services may be wanted. The right question for answer at the outset is whether there is any general faculty of attention at all—whether such a supposed faculty is not a mere notion. The truth is that there are actually as many particular attentions as there are particular subjects of attention, and no attention is ever more than a particular attitude of mind, or of that portion of the mind which is active on the particular occasion.

It is convenient to describe attention as of two kinds—namely, (a) voluntary and (b) automatic—according as the power by which it is applied comes mainly from behind (is a *vis a tergo* pushing it to the subject), or as it comes from in front (is a *vis a fronte* drawing it to the subject) ; for the distinction answers to certain broad features of its exercise. But it is not an exact and deep-reaching division, seeing that intermediate instances make a gradual transition from automatic to voluntary function. Every act of attention, even the most voluntary, presupposes an antecedent interest or attraction. When any one fixes his attention, by a strong and steady effort of

will, on a subject which has little interest for him, he
does it, not directly and independently, but by means
of intermediate related ideas which, having been
made his by previous experience, have an interest for
him.   Brought in face of the object or phenomenon,
he does not straightway pass it by without further
heed—he resolutely marks and minds it.   Why?
For the reason that, occurring among phenomena in
which he is interested in some degree—whereby, in
fact, his notice of it is solicited in the first instance—
he deliberately asks himself what relations it has to
them, if it has any, or what relations it has not to
them, if it has none; so he attends closely to it.   In
the one case it draws and fixes attention by help of
reinforcing ideas, they radiating their light upon it,
as it were, so as to make it and its affinities bright
and distinct in consciousness; in the other case it
attracts and fixes attention through the interest which
there is in demonstrating the absence of relations
where relations seem to be, being focused in consciousness by the aid of ideas with which it claims
affinities that it has no right to.

No more need be said now in order to prove how
much an attention, whether voluntary or automatic,
owes to training and habit.   Not the habit of observing one thing or doing one thing exclusively, whereby
men become automatic and go on in unvarying rounds
of thought and feeling, like so many organic machines,
falling ready into a routine of not observing or not
doing other things, but the habit of intending the
mind closely to any subject of study—the habit, that
is, of truly minding it by holding and using all related
ideas to throw light upon it.   So only will that habit
which is the power of attention grow and become
easy.   A good habit for the curious inquirer to form
would be a sceptical habit of asking why a common observation may be not a true observation, an
accepted conclusion not a sound conclusion—the rare
habit of daring to doubt and the still rarer habit of
seeing things sincerely and clearly as they are in

themselves without regard to opinions of them : for it is the custom of opinion to descend unquestioned from generation to generation, and most things continue to be believed by most people only because they have been said authoritatively and accepted mechanically, out of a passive acquiescence in received opinion and a disinclination or disability to question that which has been sanctioned by time and authority.

(d) Under the head of *bias* may be included the several active causes of fallacies of observation and reasoning which have their origin in the feelings—in the various affections, wishes, interests, passions, prejudices, fears, and tempers of human nature.

The common notion is that men get their opinions through the understanding and hold them because they are based on sound reason. Far from it : the understanding is one avenue of opinion, but another more open and more used, though disavowed, is through the feelings; the opinions so obtained demanding only from reason so much of its help as serves to excuse and support them. It is a plausible but quite false presumption that mankind in general act on rational principles. A fundamental fact of man's nature, as of all living nature, is the desire to be happy and to pursue and embrace those things which, being agreeable, make it happy; the consequence of which is a natural propensity to embrace and believe opinions that suit with desires, and to reject and disbelieve opinions that go contrary to desires. There is a vast difference between the *kind* or *quality* of the belief when it goes with, and when it goes against, desire.

To contemplate a subject in the pure white light of knowledge, without any intermixture of feeling to colour perception, is pretty nigh impossible; and the stronger the feeling which tinctures the reflection the more powerful it is as a factor in the determination of belief. It is a better way of persuasion to awaken sympathetic feeling for the weak argument than to present an irrefutable argument to an unsympathetic mind; and always the most successful way to compel belief is to kindle the congenial passion. A strong passion, by securing beforehand the suitable disposition in the individual, predisposes him to embrace and believe what is fitted to feed it. How can assimilation fail to take place when the impression from without falls into such unison with the activity within? How not agree when they are so mutually agreeable? A timid person readily believes that which greatly alarms him; the awe-struck person, what excites his awe; a suspicious person, that which jumps with his mood of suspicion; an angry person, that which seems to justify his anger to himself; a jealous person, whatsoever is in the least suited, or can anyhow be used, to feed jealousy. Always the passion, attracting congenial and reinforcing, repelling uncongenial and opposing ideas, fascinates in greater or less degree. It is only afterwards, when its tremors of activity subside, and consciousness is released from attendance on it and its ministering ideas, that uncongenial ideas have a chance of so coming into reflection as to be attended to.

It is in the emotion caused by a natural event so rare as to excite wonder, and so extraordinary as to seem supernatural, that we have the reason of the ease with which superstitious explanations of it are accepted. Observation is impossible, and the reeling mind, loosed from its moorings in familiar experience, its old patterns of perception staggered, drifts without bearings for a time, bewildered, overawed, and tremulously apprehensive; not in such complete darkness of blank ignorance as leaves the lowest savage in stupid quiet of mind, but with just so much glimmering light of dawning knowledge as makes " darkness visible " and terrible; in a very apt mood of intimidation, therefore, to believe anything of the extraordinary occurrence. Is not apprehensive expectation the natural mental mood of a being who from his birth has to fight for his life against hostile powers and in the end to lose it? There is a self-protective instinct of mind to make the overwhelming indefiniteness into something definite, to attach it somehow to the mental being; thus only is it possible to think and act in relation to it. Imagination is easily believed, therefore, when it goes to work, as it does instantly, to fill the void with superstitious explanations that are in keeping with the state of feeling and intellectual development of the race at the time and place.

Note, in this relation, how vulgar astonishment at the narration of some extraordinary event disposes to belief in it—mentally as well as physically there is gaping wonder, open-mouthed to swallow the pleasing marvel; and how prone is the narrator himself, flattered by the admiring wonder which his tale evokes and seduced by his vanity, to increase the astonishment, to supplement its defects, to exaggerate its points, to embellish its features, and to end by believing his own exaggeration! Certainly stories of the supernatural at the present day owe a main part of their authority to this cause of fallacy— to wonder-struck assent and inexact narration of inexact observation.

In like manner prophecies, presentiments, imprecations, magic incantations, predictions of witchcraft, and the like, have wrought their own accomplishment: a person has died, and that not simply as a singular coincidence, on the day it was predicted or he had a presentiment he should die; and incantation has taken fatal effect when the victim has known of and feared it; a curse has been a self-fulfilling fate when it has worked powerfully on the imagination of its subject; the physician who inspires faith and hope in his patient does more to cure him sometimes by a few harmless simples than another, unable to produce any such inspiriting effect, can do with the most fit and costly remedies. Prediction is, in the nature of things, a vastly different thing when applied to human events from what it ever is when applied to physical events: in the latter it is a passive process of simple foresight; in the former it is mind working actively on mind, so powerfully too perhaps as to fulfil itself.

With the individual, as with the race, an undisciplined egoism acts to fix a false mental standpoint, and thus to vitiate observation and lead thought astray. Every one loves his own opinions, because they are his own, better than the opinions in which he has no sense of private possession. There is always the steady bias springing necessarily from the fact of individuality. But it is when self-esteem is inflamed into passion—anger, hatred, jealousy, avarice, pride, or the like—that it forms the strongest bar to the admission of pure truth. These passions, being constituent parts of human nature, cannot be entirely eliminated from it; they work their ill effect to pervert observation and judgment, whatever the province of human labour; it is in vain to expect to get rid of them, even in the high regions of philosophy and in the dry regions of science, where they might be thought to have the least scope.

Observation is no less badly vitiated by sympathetic emotion, though in a different way. Consider how powerfully admiration, pity, and love predispose respectively to see what is admirable, to find what is deserving, to believe what is good, in the object of the feeling. Every passion naturally wishes to keep itself alive, and therefore eagerly lays hold of what feeds it. Love is proverbially blind because, seeing in its object that which it desires to see, it cannot see that which contradicts the bent of its passion; the lover infatuated because, transported out of his reason and seduced out of his senses by his passion, his observation and judgment are fatuous. Hence Plato justly included love under one sort of mania, and Shakespeare soberly describes the lover as of imagination compact with the lunatic and the poet. Moreover, as with love so with every other passion; blinding in proportion as it is engrossing, it signifies a polarization of all the molecules of the being to its object, whereby of necessity they cannot turn freely towards other objects to see and think them adequately.

It is notorious how strong and subtle a bias is given to observation and thought by wish, interest, or desire, and how hard a thing it is for the most judicial mind to go against its bias. The effect of a resolute and conscientious exercise of reason and will exactly to counteract the bias would almost certainly be to carry the judgment, by the momentum of the *nisus*, some way in the opposite direction beyond the straight line of truth; so consciously to stiffen the mental attitude as to make it unconsciously unjust. When two persons who have been witnesses of the same transaction swear to inconsistent or contradictory accounts of it, as not seldom happens, it is not usually that either of them is saying wilfully that which is not, but it is that each was so strongly biased by his wishes, interests, fears, or feelings as to see only that which was agreeable to them, or, in remembering the circumstances, to call effectively to mind only so much as suited with them. The agreements with his mood made a vivid impression and endured, the disagreements therefrom no impression, or so weak an impression that it was transient. Thus he has seen and thought what he wished, and embraced the conclusions which were grateful.

Whoso, believing in the supernatural, is eager to see signs and wonders easily sees signs and wonders himself and promptly accepts the testimony of others who attest them; it is not a wonder that he sees wonders; the real wonder would be if, being what he is, he saw not as many as he fervently expected to see. Therefore, when it is objected to the sceptic, as an unanswerable argument, that men of unimpeachable veracity and in full possession of their senses have solemnly testified that they have witnessed supernatural phenomena, he may properly, before quitting his doubts and reserve, call to mind and weigh well this pregnant truth—that two would-be truthful persons, both of whom cannot be right, will sincerely give diverse or flatly contradictory accounts of the same transaction, which they had equal means and opportunities of observing. No doubt a gross instance of manifest bias, but none the less suited to incite reflection on the manifold finer instances of its permeating influence in daily life, where it works habitually in various subtle and circuitous ways.

Whenever or wherever a supernatural event is announced the right initial attitude of mind to observe in regard to it is an attitude of stern scepticism, for so only will the tests applied to it and *all* the conditions of its occurrence be complete and rigorous. The natural reluctance to offend the pious feelings of others in such case by pushing enquiry home renders it necessary that the enquirer show no indulgence to his own feelings. He must begin his resolute scrutiny in the spirit of the indisputable truth that, while there is a strong antecedent improbability of a supernatural event in any case, there is a strong antecedent probability of a bias in favour of wish in every case, and require the elimination or invalidation of so much of the weight of authority as the evidences owes to bias. Now, as this elimination is sometimes impracticable, the only safe course, when it cannot be made, is to reject the observation ; for it will be impossible to determine truly whether it is the observation of a real thing or only the realization of a pious wish of the observer.

(*e*) A last cause of the vitiation of observation and thought to be noticed lies in the misuse and abuse of words : a common, deep, and wide-reaching cause of fallacies.

There is an inveterate proclivity to believe that a word must mean an entity, when it may be the sign of an abstraction only, and that the same word must have the same meaning, though it may have very different meanings in different mouths, and in the same mouth on different occasions. Actually the same word never has exactly the same meaning to two persons : an evil which has this useful set-off—

that differing beliefs can go on using the same name
as if they meant the same thing by it, when they
mean very different things. How widely different are
the contents of meaning of the word " matter " in the
mind of a philosopher of to-day from what the word
had in the mind of a philosopher formerly, or has now
in the mouth of the vulgar ! Although the same word
be used, the talk is not of the same thing, but of
different things under the same name. In like
manner, when the metaphysician and the physiologist
dispute about mind, the discussion is barren from its
beginning, since they speak not really of the same
thing ; they have no common ground of understanding, nor even a language in common ; the store of
experience and reflections which the one has accumu-
lated being useless to the other because based on a
theory of mind which he thinks absurd, and expressed
in language which has no meaning to him.

How much, or rather how little, is there actually in
common between the early Christian, despised member of a mean and persecuted sect in the midst of a
hostile community, and the Christian of to-day, the
all-triumphant member of a dominant and aggressive
religion which summons artillery to support its invasions and armies to avenge its repulses ? It is a contrast, not a comparison of faiths, intellectually and
morally, that we are in face of ; the two beings,
although professing the same religion and called by
the same name, being no more like as concrete
believers than two persons of entirely different religions and civilizations. The one shrank not from
dying a martyr's death for his faith, the other has
seldom faith enough to prevent his shrinking from
dying a natural death.

Language is the specialized expression or denotation
by vocal sounds and written signs—the muscular
denomination, so to speak—of feelings, ideas, and
their associations. Having been framed in accordance with vulgar experience it necessarily stirs corresponding associations ; for which reason it cannot be

used scientifically in the vulgar sense when such use gives rise to inadequate or erroneous associations. How are men to obtain new and true apprehension of a class of facts that have been misapprehended, or not apprehended at all, when the language used to describe them, implying and endorsing old and erroneous opinions of them, inevitably evokes misleading associations? How so use the faulty instrument, as if it had no fault, to perform that exact apprehension and expression which, by very reason of its fault, it is not fitted to perform? Until new and truer associations have been formed by the progress of related knowledge it is impossible to have the new facts and relations apprehended rightly and their language exactly defined.

It is a common dictum, transformed into an axiom by frequent and confident repetition, that no nation, be it never so savage or barbarous, has existed without some notion of a God; and the allegation is thereupon adduced as strong evidence of the existence of a God. Granting the untrue statement to be true, for the sake of argument, is it not a monstrous misuse of words to use the same term to denote notions so widely different as those which a cultivated European and a low savage entertain of God, and to assume tacitly that they are notions of the same thing? Let a clear and exact definition be made of that which the word is thought to signify in each case; then let the definition of the European's God be substituted mentally for the word on each occasion when the God of the savage is spoken of, and the definition of the savage's savage God substituted mentally on each occasion when the civilized person's civilized God is spoken of—it is instantly and plainly manifest that little or nothing is true of the one which is true of the other. So far from identity, there is barely a similarity of objects; the mental substitution is not a substitution of similars, which is the basis of true reasoning, but a substitution of dissimilars, which is necessarily the cause of false reasoning. It is incredible how many vain disputes arising out of the entanglements of words would collapse instantly were the disputants to have clear definitions of their terms and to substitute mentally the definitions for the terms in their reasonings; were they to keep resolutely in mind the sagacious saying of Hobbes, that " words are the counters of wise men and the money of fools."

A second fruitful cause of error in the use of words is the assumption, tacit or express, that the word must mean a thing. There have been few, if any, more pregnant causes of errors in philosophy than the tendency to make words things by projecting named abstractions of the mind into nature as entities, and thereafter treating them as if they were active agents there. Nature is misapprehended, and of the misapprehensions are made principles or entities in it—metaphysical entities to do duty as explanations of events, though not explanations at all, being no more than restatements of the facts in more abstract terms : a principle or spirit of phlogiston to explain the phenomena of combustion ; a soporific principle to account for the narcotic virtues of opium ; a vital principle to preside over the phenomena of life ; a spiritual principle to uphold the high dignity of mental phenomena. To which, indeed, might be added *an* attention to attend, *a* memory to remember, *an* imagination to imagine, *a* reason to reason, *a* will to will, *a* consciousness to be conscious.

It is one of the merits of Kant to have first clearly demonstrated to psychologists that all notions and beliefs respecting the order of nature, though not innate but derived from experience, are conditioned necessarily by the innate *forms* of human thought. These forms experience does not supply; they are innate in the constitution of mind, the indispensable conditions of its experience, not otherwise than as the forms of bodily movements are conditioned by the constitution and dispositions of its muscles. It was very useful work at the time, and the need of it in philosophy greater then than it is easy for a physiologist to conceive now; but some of his modern disciples go far to treat forms of thought as if they had existence and meaning in themselves, apart from their contents, and as if they were in no sense relative, like thoughts, but had independent being and absolute value.

The common way of thinking and speaking of a law of nature exemplifies a fallacy of the same kind. The law is pictured as a sort of objective power ruling despotically in its domain of nature and constraining things to obey it, whereas it is no more, rightly viewed, than the general statement of experience that things go in a certain definite course. The executive force is not in the law, but in the nature of the thing in its relations to other things. The law is simply the generalization of observation, no more than the general statement or subjective formula of a certain order of events, and may be right or wrong, complete or incomplete. The erroneous notion of law as itself a cogent agency in nature has been derived from the notion of rule or law laid down by human enactment and enforced by due executive authority; and from law understood in that sense the transition was natural and easy to a lawgiver in the universe, working after human methods and made in the magnified image of man.

A conclusion of the same kind is the familiar conclusion from intelligence and reason in man to supernatural intelligence and reason. As though limitation were not of the very essence of intelligence and reason, and these functions could be anything more than a relative being's classified experience of a very limited range of natural things and their relations, or were terms of real meaning, other than literal nonsense, when used in relation to an absolute Being in whom all things are comprehended. It would be no more absurd to attribute to Him labour and rest, as indeed primitive theology did. How can any predication concerning the supernatural by the natural possibly be anything but a meaningless proposition? Nay, when we ponder it, what else but prodigious blasphemy is it to speak at all of the reason of God, whose knowledge must plainly be intuitive, not discursive? He cannot be supposed to work to an *end* in lame human fashion by labouring steps and inferences of reason; must, as all-seeing and infinite, see the remote in the present, the end in the beginning, the universal and eternal in the instant.

Many more illustrations of the power of names over things, or rather over the thoughts and feelings about things, might be cited here were it necessary, since the history of thought in every department of nature teems with them. At one time, in medicine, any fancied sign of likeness in a drug or in its name to something in a disease or in a disease's name was thought to be nature's seal of its efficacy in that disease, and in country districts nettle-tea (*Urtica*, nettle) is still the popular remedy for nettle-rash (*Urticaria*).

Among all nations, in all places and times, ill-meaning words have been dreaded as likely to bring misfortune. To the ancient Romans the ill omen boded by the names was good reason for changing the name of *Maleventum* into *Beneventum*, of *Epidamnum* into *Dyrrachium*; a contagion of evil was feared in them. It is a general, if not natural, impulse to shrink from speaking of a person's death in his presence, or in the presence of his friends, or even in any one else's presence; rather than use the actual word people go about to indicate, by some kind of ambiage, what may not be said expressly; and in different nations all sorts of euphemisms are in use for this purpose, just as if the word " death," the moment it left the speaker's lips, was a fateful power to fulfil itself.* Few are the persons who can divest

---

* Although a general, it is not a universal, impulse; for the Chinese meet death with the greatest coolness; and nothing is more gratifying to the dying man than to see that a handsome coffin has been prepared for him. See Abbé Huc's *Chinese Empire.*

themselves of the superstitious feeling that there is something more than an explosion of vain words, some power more than natural, some mysterious executive fatality, in a parent's curse of a disobedient child, though the child hear it not, or in the victim's dying appeal to God against his murderer.   Believing that the universe must be in sympathy with human affairs, they discover in the passionate invocation of vengeance the prophetic pledge of its fulfilment.

So much, then, in exemplification of the errors of belief that have flowed from the natural defects of human observation and reasoning.   It is abundantly evident that most of the superstitious beliefs and practices which have come and gone through the human past have had their source and sustenance in these defects.   Once inevitable as the gropings of infantile thought, such superstitions and errors, having outlived the reason of their being, persist now as survivals of a lower level of intelligence.   Being degradations of thought, in the sense of belonging to lower grades of thought, they are therefore displayed in civilized countries chiefly by those who are so engrossed in the supply of their daily wants that they have not the leisure or inclination to train and cultivate their minds in correct habits of thought, and in relation to those subject-matters of thought that lie furthest from the reach of human apprehension.

CHAPTER III

IMAGINATION: ITS NATURE AND FUNCTION

A RICH source of wrong beliefs is the prolific activity of imagination ever prompt and pleased to exercise itself. Hastening off-hand to meet the instinctive desire to believe, by filling up voids of knowledge with fictions and theories, its quick and easy working is in striking contrast with the slow and toilsome work of observation and reasoning. Being the productive force in mind, it has, like the productive force in nature, three marked qualities: it is prolific, it is pleasant, it is prophetic.

Its fertility is in effect inexhaustible, although most of the innumerable products thereof perish, one here and there only in the prodigality of production being destined to live and grow to maturity. Just as the individual plant or animal in the course of its life generates a countless multitude of germs—as many, indeed, as would, were they all to reach maturity, suffice to make a numerous species, perhaps to populate a continent; so the individual imagination is perpetually conceiving germs of thought which, were they soundly based and fitly placed, might equal in number all the true thoughts that a nation has had from the cradle to the grave of its being.

Why is there so much more pleasure in the easy exercise of imagination making fiction than in the labouring work of reason welding truths? It is an instance of the pleasure and spontaneity belonging to the function of generation everywhere in nature. Generation or creation, in poetry, in painting, in sculpture, in invention, in any other art—ποίησις, that is to say, of any sort—is its function; it shares, therefore, in the transport or ecstasy which accompanies procreation throughout nature : a transport of it alike whether it work well to generate good progeny, or work ill to generate sickly deformities of imagination and rickety deformities of bodies—the depravities of a vicious imagination or the degenerate offspring of a vitiated parentage.

As it is indispensable for imagination to be well and truly informed in order to create truly, to have the good nurture of a sound experience of things and the controlling rules of a right understanding, no one can have a sound imagination without a sound reason, or train his imagination to form rightly except through his reason. Of itself it cannot correct its own work— *that* reason must do ; for, like a fond mother doting on her deformed offspring, it is just as pleased with its bad as its good births.

The wild abuse of imagination ought not to hinder its sober and proper use. For a long time to come it is certain that men will be unsatisfied to stay in a quiet repose and confession of ignorance as to what lies beyond the reach of thought ; urged by an insatiable curiosity to know, they will chafe against the bar to new leaps of knowledge and strive to surmount it. And justly, seeing that without speculative curiosity there would be no enquiry, without enquiry no theories or hypotheses, without theories or hypotheses no increase of knowledge. Definite guesses at truth are what great discoverers like Kepler and Faraday avowedly make in order to look definitely for it, throwing many aside as worthless for every one which stands the test of verification and, being proved, they hold fast ; for it is not the duty of the scientific enquirer to abstain from framing hypotheses, as some ignorantly maintain, his duty is to make as many likely guesses as he can, rejecting the bad ones, until he has made the right guess and proved it right by the full tests of experiment and reflection. His process is nothing else but the application of the common process of vulgar enquiry to special fields of study.

In estimating the value of the products of imagination it is most necessary to take account of the conditions under which it works and of the limitations imposed on its workings. The principal considerations to be weighed in mind are these—(a) The common causes of error of observation and reasoning; (b) the native structure and special moods of the individual mind; (c) the natural limits of human understanding.

(a) Inasmuch as imagination does not create out of the void, but forms as it has been informed, its contents witness unavoidably to the modes of thought and feeling of the age, of the people, and of the person. As in times of old, fashioning after the fashion of the time, it filled nature with demons and deities, more or less monstrously human in character; as in later times it created metaphysical entities out of mental abstractions in order to have species of agents to do what, being ignorant of the real natural agencies, men could not imagine to be done without them; so now, demons being dead and metaphysical entities in desperate case everywhere save in journals and class-rooms of mental philosophy, it luxuriates in theories that forerun and too often forestall sound observation and inference in the various fields of scientific enquiry. If the devil of to-day is a very different person in the Christian imagination from the devil of the middle ages, having undergone a marvellous evolutional metamorphosis, it is not because he has really changed in hell with the changes on earth—it is because the mental image of him has undergone change in proportion as men have come to know more and to imagine less about the real forces and regular order of external nature.

In like manner a gradual modification of the conception of God has taken place so quietly yet so completely as to be a virtual transformation of one thing into another under the same name. The Jehovah of the Jews was a special God—jealous, angry, revengeful, repenting Him that He had made man, execrating the rashness which had sworn that He would not destroy him, greedy of adoration and sacrifice; a Being to be flattered by appeals to His vanity as Lord of lords and King of all gods, among the heathen none like unto Him, and to be moved by provoking His jealousy of other gods; who walked and talked and argued with men, commanding them to do the most atrocious acts of murder, cruelty, fraud, and rapine, and rewarding those who obediently did them because they had done according to His heart that which was right in His sight; in fact, a thoroughly immoral God from the standpoint of modern reason and humanity, albeit a Godhead suited at the time to the semi-barbarous mind and character of His chosen people, and most helpful to their national unity and growth.

This crude conception was gradually refined and sublimed through later Jewish history, being so transformed by the Psalmist and the Prophets that the transition was easy to the Christian conception of God —the God no longer now of a section of mankind, but of the whole human race; not a tyrant, but a Father in Heaven, All-mighty and All-merciful, who, grieving for disobedient children fallen from grace into disgrace, yet yearning to redeem them from damnation, deemed the incarnation in human form, and the vicarious sacrifice of His only-begotten Son by a lingering death on the cross, the costly means necessary for their restoration to His favour.

As the Jew conceived his God after the fashion of his thought and feeling, so the Christian conceived his God as he thought and felt; and the conceptions are necessarily widely different. Those who, not being Jews nor Christians, perceive evidence of human manufacture in both images, may still discern in the Christian imagination two rational ideas carried to irrational extremes—first, an apotheosis of the natural principle of atonement which rules in the social body, whereby one member inevitably suffers for another's sins, the just for the unjust, and reaps the fruits of another's virtues, the unjust of the just; secondly, an exaggeration of human self-esteem to a sort of megalomania, whereby man counted himself of such transcendent worth in the universe as to have needed and imagined so unique a redemption.

As the evolution of the conception of God has gone on from age to age, not continuing in one state, it is no surprise that the once-authorized version is not accepted by all Christians at the present day. Not a few, whose numbers increase steadily, now abandon altogether the notion of a personal God of any kind, retreating into a vague Theism, which differs little if at all, except in name, from Pantheism or Atheism.

(b) Again, it is obvious that the natural temper and present mood of the mind affect powerfully the character of the imagination.

The roots of imagination lie so deep in feeling that its ideals bespeak essential character. Not the distinguishing temper of each mind only, but even organic character; for its inspiring moods may be said to express the concurrence, in conscious outcome, of the multitudinous infraconscious vibrations of the organic nature. Thus sane and whole imagination bespeaks a sane and whole organization; sickly and degenerate imagination, a defective or degenerate organization.

Persons of like neurotic temperaments show like frenzies of imagination in fanatical schemes of reform, social, philanthropic, or political. So exclusively are they engrossed with the merits of the aim they have in eager view that they see nothing right in anything opposed to it, nothing wrong in anything which serves to further it. They are fascinated, hypnotized by it; so "overlooked," so to speak, or enthralled by the "evil eye" of the fixed idea, that they are mentally blind to qualifying reasons and opposing evidence.

A further effect of the exclusive and excessive neurotic strain which he fosters is a disintegration of the moral nature; like a hysterical or a hypnotized person similarly disorganized mentally, and similarly unaware of his disorganization, he cannot then see and feel and speak the truth, and knows not when he is seeing, feeling, and speaking untruth. So it comes to pass that, rabidly earnest on the subject of his special passion, he is still capable of no little habitual guile, vice, perhaps even crime, without being the conscious or feeling himself the actual hypocrite which he looks to outsiders. Being an extraordinary person inspired to do extraordinary work, he is exempt from the common rules of morality; having christened his vice zeal he indulges it as a virtue. Those who are in league of fanatical sympathy with him may not be expected to confess, even can they see, the fault in him as they would be prompt to see it in an outsider. To them the vice, however ugly it looks, is in him only an unsphered virtue gone pitifully astray.

When a mental organization is disintegrated or, so to speak, dismembered, whether artificially by experiment, or by bad training, or by disease, and perforce therefore demoralized, it functions not as a whole, but in disjointed parts which are not responsible for one another; wherefore unity and consistency of moral feeling are impossible, and the individual can do immoral things without being rationally conscious of and fully responsible for them. All the more dispossessed of self is he when he is inflamed by enthusiasm, which is a sort of ignition or flaming agitation of mind whereby the particular tract of passionate thought is thrown entirely out of gear. The special imagination of the fanatic denoting this exclusive set of his whole energies to its bent and a deadening or suspending of all impressions which are not or which it cannot turn in unison with it, the natural effect is to attribute more certainty to its vivid representations than to the sober impressions of experience : an effect all the more powerful because of the delirious delight which usually attends such a rapture of disjointed thought. For it is not merely the exalted thought which is in excess, the accompanying feeling is similarly rapt in ecstasy. Deeming itself then spiritual, though it is essentially irrational, the ravished or ecstatic tract cannot choose but feel its intense experience to be more real and credible than things visible; going on perhaps in process of further morbid development to see visions, to hear voices from heaven, and to enter into direct communion with the supernatural. Thus it is that enthusiasm becomes the accredited evidence and utterance of religious truths.

The world is wise to make the best use it can of such fiery zeal and energy, since it may properly use every tool for what it is worth; but it is not wise to discover a divine afflatus in the inspiration of the frenzy. Where is the wit of adoring fervour because it is fervour, when it is the fervour of disease? To do that, what is it but to go tamely back to the superstition once prevalent everywhere, and still extant somewhere, that there was special divine working in the convulsions of epilepsy and in the delirium of madness? However laudable the inspiration of the fanatic's frenzy, one ought not to overlook the hysteria and the delirium there is in it; and that, so far from being holy in the fundamental sense of healthy, is really unholy because unhealthy. A few more steps lower in degeneration, a few more steps higher in the conceit of an exalted mission, a little increase in the grandiose ideas, a little keener the exasperation of suspicions of hostility—and this kind of neuropathic fanatic, mounting in self-esteem, sinks into a well-defined category of madness.

CHAPTER IV

IMAGINATION : ITS ILLUSIONS

WHILE justly admitting how exceeding finite is the known in comparison with the infinite unknown, and what an endless domain imagination has to play in, it is quite another thing to accept any one of the different interpretations of the unknown which imagination has from time to time devised. Such interpretations have notoriously reflected the moods and modes of thought of the people who devised them. In the respective features of two leading forms of superstition which have prevailed among mankind there is a striking illustration of two opposite attitudes of mind in relation to the supernatural, inspired by opposite tempers and inspiring opposite interpretations. On the one hand, as outcome of the dejected mood, a gloomy imagination created all-powerful gods or demons of malignant disposition, before whom the trembling mortal fell prostrate in abject fear and abasement, striving to move their pity, to appease their anger, to propitiate their favour by the most tedious ceremonial, the most painful observances, the most costly sacrifices : just the attitude of an abject slave abasing himself to the utmost before an Eastern despot and adoring him in language of fulsome flattery, or that of a fawning dog before an angry master, whom it strives to propitiate by its cringing humility. A survival of that attitude lingers still in the appointed day of humiliation, fasting, and prayer. On the other hand, as outcome of the exalted mood of mind, an inflamed imagination transported the mortal into a state in which he believed himself in communion with the supernatural being, perhaps descended from it by miraculous generation, and

invested with a divine commission to lead, guide, and
govern mankind. Himself persuaded and persuading
the multitude that he is the chosen organ of divine
function, he then poses as a mediator between men
and the hidden unknown God—the *Deus absconditus*—
who can tell them what the God wants of them, and
how He may be best propitiated with sacrifice and
service.

Having this twofold function as a mediator between
two different and absolutely separate orders of being,
divine and human, it was necessary to have a twofold nature, divine and human, and, in further logical
sequence, sometimes a parentage half divine and half
human. For how could he mediate between them if
he did not share the two separate natures ? So sprang
up the fable of the amorous god descending from
Olympus in mysterious guise to impregnate the virgin
who then conceived and brought forth the hero. In
this way various religions of the world have had their
several mediators and prophets, inferior to the god yet
superior to the man, and have owed to the supernatural sanction much of their authority and binding
force.

It is curious to see how mankind has contrived to
save itself from itself, and, so to speak, in spite of
itself ; for it has neutralized a humiliating order of
superstition, which might have paralysed its progress,
by an exalting order of superstition which animated and
impelled it. By the special organs which it was able
to develop from time to time in the shapes of special
quasi-inspired prophets, it reacted successfully against
the prostration of abject superstitious fear and a
demoralizing paralysis of its powers. Having damned
itself by a dejected exercise of imagination when
powerless in face of the unknown forces and terrors of
nature, it redeemed itself by an exalted exercise of it
when observation and reflection had imparted some
sense of power and dignity.

All accounts of savage and barbarous tribes go to
show that it was the strong man, whether in war, in

hunting, or in council, who was made a chief and thereafter obeyed : loosely and partially perhaps amongst the lowest savages, but with almost absolute submission by those who had reached a higher level of social organization. When the chief united in himself the ruling and the priestly functions his position as mediator between his people and the supernatural power, and as sole interpreter of its decrees, could not fail to impart a singular sanction to his authority. In the natural progress of organic development from the general to the special, these functions after a while became specialized and had their separate ministers; among savage peoples a special order of medicine-men, and among higher peoples a special order of priests, became the exclusive agents of the supernatural.

Those who have watched closely the doings of the medicine-men among savages are pretty well agreed that they are impostors, who, having inherited the mysteries of their craft and being to the manner born and trained, practise it for their profit. Looking on it as their professional means of livelihood in the community, they think it part of the natural order of things and quite as legitimate as any other means of livelihood : cannot see it in its true nature as the practical lie which it is. Their conscience does not condemn even so much of the fraud as it is conscious of. How can they who have not risen to the height of moral sense have sense of the morality of truth ? They give the people value for their money, and give it in the only coin which has value for them : what use would it be to give them coin which, not being current, would be useless to them ? If nine-tenths of the human nature they have to do with is folly and ignorance, it would show a want of wisdom to deal with it strictly as if it were wisdom. The impracticable idealist who thought to do that might justly reckon with his own impotence and possible martyrdom.

Imposture will not be fairly judged by the judgment which assumes unity and consistency to be necessary qualities of a mind. Nothing could be more contrary to the truth; for there is not an inconsistency of belief or conduct of which human nature is not capable. The augur who discharges his professional functions, believing in the self which he then is, is quite another self from what he is when, not being on duty, he laughs with his fellow augurs at the comedy in which he plays his part; or perhaps laughs not quite sincerely, since he is so much two inconsistent selves that he takes himself seriously in both. When he puts on the uniform of his holy office he puts on at the same time the uniform of his belief and dignity, and thereupon, like a judge or a policeman, instantly feels and expresses the authority which his office inspires in himself and others. A judge in his shirt-sleeves might be a capable judge and deliver better judgments than an incapable judge dressed in wig and ermine; but he would feel less judicial and do less justice probably, seeing that it is the opinion of things, not the things in themselves, that mankind most regards. Moreover, a habit of belief and action ingrained in germ by tradition becomes by use and wont a second nature; so that, though contrary to all reason, it may keep its irrational place in an otherwise rational mind independently of—indeed, in defiance of—the customary operations of reason and conscience and without being troubled by them. There is a good deal to be said, then, in explanation and excuse of the imposture of the medicine-man when he performs his office of messenger and mediator between the natural and the supernatural.

Among the ancient Egyptians the inner secrets of knowledge and faith were purposely shrouded in mystery and carefully hidden from the vulgar. One may suspect that Moses, being bred up in all their traditional learning, profited by this knowledge in the skilful use which he made of his alleged interviews with the Deity in order to impose his authority on the Israelites. Two things it is difficult to believe now: first, that Moses ever had the conversations or the partial personal interview with Jehovah which he is reported to have had; secondly, that he was ever so possessed and dominated by hallucinations as actually to believe that he had them.   Those, therefore, who reject not the history as mythical, may believe that, after the manner of the Egyptian priesthood, in whose secrets he had been initiated, he beguiled the people for their good, inflaming their hopes and zeal with the belief of supernatural aid and guidance, and sparing them the knowledge of the formidable difficulties they would have to encounter.   However great his insincerity of speech in his capacity of actor, Moses evinced a thorough sincerity and veracity of insight into the thing as it was in his dealing with men as their leader; not only in seeing definitely what he had to do and the definite means of doing it, but in the frank acknowledgment to himself that the rational use of the fit means involved the treatment of the ignorant and foolish multitude according to its folly.   Had he not condescended to the level of their understanding, most certainly he never could have incited and inveigled the Israelites to go through with the mighty enterprise which he had conceived for their welfare, and been the successful leader he was until, age having sapped his decision and energy, he was supplanted and suppressed by Joshua.   After all is said, be it in praise or blame, the successful man of action on men is compelled to put on something of the charlatan in order to impress the vulgar imagination, always so ready to be impressed that it is often satisfied with the charlatanry without the genius. Excellent as are the common precepts of morality for human nature's daily uses, still it fails not to make its greatest heroes of the men who, in mightily managing it, have unscrupulously trampled on its moral rules.

Take another of the triad of great prophets treated of by that " villain and secretary of hell " (as Sir Thomas Browne rudely calls him in his remarkable essay *De Tribus Impostoribus*)—to wit, Mahomet. Is it credible that Mahomet ever had or believed he

c

had the wonderful supernatural experiences which he professed to have? Despite a postulated necessity of sincerity and veracity in the man who did the great work he did, one may take leave to think that the veracity he had was the veracity to see and use the necessary means by which his countrymen, being what they were then and there, could be best moved and used. If the story be true that when, by way of performing a miracle, he commanded the mountain to come to him, and, the mountain making no motion, quietly remarked that if the mountain would not come to Mahomet then Mahomet must go to the mountain, what stronger proof could there be of his sanity of judgment, of his strength of character, and—it is no breach of charity to add—of his silent contempt for the credulity of his followers? Could he have shown more clearly that he was not himself imposed on by the stories which beguiled them for his purpose and their good? Sincerity and veracity by all means, only let it be the sincerity to see that the majority represents a preponderance of folly which must be managed after its kind, and the veracity to deal with fools as the facts which they are. Rational imagination appeals in vain to irrational imagination; but fanaticism applied to folly quickly makes a blaze.

As the domain of the supernatural has now been reduced to a small field for the exercise of imagination, its post-scientific is much more sober than its pre-scientific work was wont to be. It seems hardly credible that it should ever have invented what it did and that men should ever have believed what it invented. Where are the gods of Hamath and of Arpad? Of Sepharvaim, Hena, and Ivah? Where the gods of Greece and of Rome? Of India and of Mexico? The devil who, in the early days of Christianity, roamed about like a roaring lion seeking whom he might devour—where roams he now? The grotesque devil of the Middle Ages and the more human-like Satan of Milton's conception have both faded into fables of imagination. Not one of these dead supernatural beings could live in the mental atmosphere of the present day; being the work of imagination weaving the coarse vestures of crude thinking, they are the spectres now of departed faiths. To modern Christian thought and feeling the devil and hell in any imaginable shapes are becoming an encumbrance which it would be a relief to get rid of by relegation to the decent oblivion of an obsolete allegory; they were suited formerly to an immature, they are unsuited now to a maturer, understanding.

As many gods have been superseded by one god in the course of human evolution, so the conception of the one god has undergone, and still undergoes, change. Monotheism in name means not the worship of the same god in fact, not even when it is professedly the worship of the same god. Different as were the original conceptions of the Jewish and the Christian gods, Jew and Christian profess now to worship one and the same God. But they do nothing of the kind. It is the name only which is the same. As the Jew is still in expectation of the Messiah to come specially to His people, rejecting Jesus Christ as an impious impostor, while the Christian believes the rejected Christ was not only the true Messiah promised to the Jews, but the incarnate Son of God, of one substance with God, it is evident that they cannot, when they go beneath the name to think sincerely what it signifies, believe that they worship the same God. They have their separate keys to separate heavens, and can hardly look frankly into one another's eyes, if they are sincere, without thinking that they are severally damned. All the while they do look into one another's eyes without drawing the inevitable conclusion.

It is no wonder, then, that the tendency of modern thought in Christendom, impatient of self-stultification in futile endeavours to conceive the inconceivable, is to refine and subtilize the conception of God, making it more and more abstract, until every element of personality has been eliminated from it. " An abstract supernatural omnipotence " which created

all things in the beginning and, having started them
on their foreordained way, has not interfered since
with their ordered course—such is the remote abstraction, suspended in ever-receding dimness, which the
Christian theologian postulates as a necessity of
philosophic thought. Such too the ingenuity by
which men can contrive to accept the entire transformation or dissolution of a belief so long as the label
of it is left intact; such the moral legerdemain by
which they reconcile themselves to go on reciting its
fables as literal truths, and performing their functions
as ministers and stewards of its mysteries.

In another field of thought imagination has wrought
with great effect to build and keep up a belief of
personal immortality. The belief, strong and sacred
as it seems, is not now, nor ever was, universal among
mankind. There have always been savages utterly
destitute of it; the Jews were without it during a
long period of their history; one sect of them, the
Sadducees, continued to the last to hold that there was
no resurrection. The Buddhist immortality, whatever else it may be, is an annihilation of self; and,
among Christian peoples who hold the belief most
surely, there have always been individuals, and those
not the least thoughtful, who have rejected it absolutely
as the fond fiction of human egoism. Moreover, were
the belief the universal thing which some theologians
would like it to be, and like, therefore, in spite of
evidence, to believe and assert it to be, the fact would
not be absolute warrant of the truth of it.

A truth, though unwelcome, ought not to be rejected
because it is repugnant to the feelings of those who
love illusion and live gladly in the illusion they love.
He who has been a frequent witness of the actual
process of dying cannot but wonder at the pre-
posterous fables which excited imaginations have
constructed about the death-bed. Fear-stricken imagination is then swift to dominate the observations
of sense and the reflections of reason. The sorrowful
attendants on the sad scene, being anxious, agitated,

and full of fear in watching the near approach of
death, ascribe to the dying person desires and feelings
and fears which they, strong in life, have and think he
must have; albeit he, being nearly dead, has them not
nor can possibly have them. They imagine how they
would feel if, feeling as they do now, they were in his
situation, forgetting that in such much different conditions they, so different, would not and could not
possibly have their present feelings. Any chance-
utterance of the dying man's—a simple exclamation
or a delirious cry, coherent or incoherent—they
eagerly catch and interpret in the terms of their own
excited feelings and imaginations, and thus entirely
misinterpret; discover in the muttered word " peace "
not the simple wish to be left at peace, but the express
assurance of a peace which passeth understanding; in
the cry for more light because of the darkness of failing
sight a fore-glimpse of heavenly light; in the last
flicker of expiring memory reviving a long-lost face
or voice of childhood a vision or voice from the
spiritual world; in the ripple of an uncertain smile
across the face, as automatic as the reflex visceral smile
of a sleeping baby, the joy-sign of a celestial glory-
peep.

Meanwhile the actual state of the dying person is
most often one of persistent belief that he will recover,
at any rate will not die this time, until he is so ill as
actually dying to be incapable of knowing that it is
death; or it is one of dull indifference to what is
going on around, a semi-somnolent apathy, as if it
were some scene enacted at a distance, half shadowy,
in which he had only a dream-like remote concern;
or it is, occasionally but rarely, a passionate prayer
for the relief of death when he suffers the fierce pains
of an acute agony or the long weary weakness of a
tediously protracted agony.

It would be more true generally to speak of the
imagination than of the belief of immortality. For the
most part it is but a half-belief, the sort of partial
belief which many persons notoriously cannot help

feeling for a popular superstition which at heart they believe not. Had Christians the genuine belief which they wish and think to have, they never could live as they do in practical negation of it; live—as for the most part they have always done—as if this brief life were all in all, while professing to look forward to an eternal life of retribution for the deeds done in it. By their deeds, not by their creeds, are they rightly judged.

If it be alleged that the death of the body is not death wholly, but the release of an imprisoned spirit from its bodily tenement and its entrance then, in the form of an invisible spiritual body, on a higher life of some kind in a higher sphere somewhere, that is a statement which does not rest on observation of nature. No one has ever seen, touched, or had other sensible evidence of the independent spirit in man, nor has it ever been detected in the act of quitting the body with the last breath. The latest psychophysical investigations of experimental psychology have not hitherto demonstrated any such departure. As the knowledge of the departing soul has not come by outward observation, so neither has it been gained by self-observation; for certainly no one can speak from his own experience of a spirit apart from the body, much less of its departure from his body at the moment of death.

It is absurd to cite as evidence in this matter the opinion which primitive people had and some barbarous people still hold—namely, that the spirit leaves the body during dreams and ecstasies and delirium to make journeys on its own account, returning home to it when the dream or ecstasy or delirium is over; for the riper understanding of man perceives what unripe understanding could not perceive, that everybody's external world is in his mind, not his mind in the external world. When thought wings its instant flight from London to Pekin it does not go very far; it travels only from one nerve-track in the brain to another so close to it that a microscope is needed to demonstrate their separateness. Naturally, therefore, it takes no longer time to travel from London to Pekin than from London to York. Certainly the teaching of natural observation, objective and introspective, is emphatic to show that in this world mind comes into being with the body, grows with its growth, matures with its maturity, sickens with it in sickness, decays with it in decay, dies with it in death. It was not the light of labouring reason, but the flash of illuminating faith, which infused the assurance of immortality; the conviction, therefore, survives by faith in spite and defiance of reason.

How prodigious, if we think of it, the amazing conceit that the whole universe—sun, moon, stars, and all the hosts of heaven, known and unknown—were created in order that one of the most insignificant of the planets might serve as a theatre for man and his doings such as he and they have been and promise still to be, and that every single being who has ever drawn breath since human breathing began will live for ever and ever. What a mighty prodigality of means for so mean an end !

The truth of course is that men do not believe it, however eagerly they hasten to say and think they do ; not one among them could live for a day as he lives if he really believed it. Happy to indulge a vague notion of an abstract kind of indefinite existence in an indefinite somewhere, without daring to realize to themselves what the peopling of eternity means in the concrete, they conciliate the profession of hazy belief with a life of very practical disbelief and carefully cultivate a voluntary ignorance of their hypocrisy. The history of mankind, like the history of the individual, is the true story of its belief; and that is a history of practical unbelief in a future life, for it is the history of a truceless struggle to get the best of this life.

CHAPTER V

IMAGINATION : ITS PHYSICAL BASIS

WHAT is the nervous substratum of imagination?
That is a question which he must perforce ask himself
who knows that nervous substratum it must have,
and wishes to form clear and distinct ideas of its
true basis, of its rational development, and of the
conditions of its sound exercise. The pre-essential
requisite to a definite answer is to clear the mind of
the metaphysical notion that there is any such being
or thing as *the* imagination ; to realize distinctly that
the name is only a general term to include a great
number and variety of particular imaginations, and
that there is no imagination apart from each particular act of imagination. The right question therefore
always is, What is the particular nervous substratum
of a particular imagination?

It is now an accepted physiological doctrine that the
substratum of a thought is a nervous tract represent-
ing, at a higher cerebral remove, a sensory nerve
connected by a nerve-centre with a motor nerve ; a
reflex arc, so to speak, along which the proper nervous
current runs in the cerebral plane. How, then, can
imagination have any place or part in a process which,
though it may be strong or weak, quick or slow, cannot
go off its own track, cannot in fact transcend the
experience which has informed it? When imagination works to create something new, something
beyond known experience, it is a specious, if not
necessary, surmise that there is a formation of new
nerve-junctions or nerve-tracks between the old
stocks or tracks of thought, by the bringing into use,
for the formation of such junctions, of nerve-cells

that lie about in all stages of incomplete development ; that is to say, if the intervention of a nerve-cell and its processes be necessary, as assumed, to effect a junction of nerve-tracks. For if one idea means a current of activity along a particular nerve-track and another idea another current along another track in the cerebral cortex, it is clear that, when an unexpected relation is suddenly revealed between two ideas hitherto looked on as unrelated, a communication between the two tracks—functional if not structural —must have been made : the novelty of thought demands a novelty of nerve-current. When two currents run along nerve-tracks into adjacent nerve-terminals where, so far as can be seen, the nerve loses its isolating sheath and ends indistinguishably in the tissue, it may be that, accumulating there, they attain by intensification or by nearness of approach such an attraction of affinity that they rush together across the intervening matter and make a new path of function : a new temporary line of communication through contiguity or contact when the imagination is a transient fantasy, a duly organized track when it is a well-grounded organic imagination.*

Two different ideas or different qualities of them joined together so as to constitute a new conception —*that* is the fundamental type of imagination in invention, in art, in poetry, in science. Its lowest exercise is the incongruous joining of things without real relations in their natures, as when the head and neck of a man are joined to the body of a horse, thus

---

* A transient flash of motion certainly in the first instance, which might be an induced current, seeing that oftentimes a thought hardly conceived, and not pursued, or, if conceived, not recorded at the moment, escapes and is lost for ever. It is not perhaps in mechanical and visible paths of conduction, but in the invisible subtilties of electrical physics, that we must seek the true analogies of cerebral function. Neither contact nor continuity of structure may be needed for one nervous current to excite another ; the process may resemble the excitation of an electric current in one wire by that in another some distance off.

making a Centaur : a childlike performance of grotesque art attesting prolific energy of it without the basis of substantial reason. At a higher level comes fancy, yoking things or qualities together temporarily by superficial traits of resemblance, without regard to fundamental quality and essential likeness; which revels therefore in whimsical and fugitive associations, fanciful metaphors, sportive sallies, ingenious artifices, is abundantly playful, but not truly productive. At highest level stands truly informed imagination which, nourished by the best reason and sensible to the deepest affinities of things, organically unites essential qualities of them, thus creating a product which is a living addition to the structure and life of the mental organization : something more perfect than individual experience and in harmony with all possible experiences of its kind, a perfectly mathematical mental synthesis of its kind. If fertile combinations of ideas, flashes of new conceptions, prophetic anticipations of experience, represent new forming associations between appropriate nerve-tracks, the formed structure displayed outwardly by the poet in his poem, by the sculptor in his sculpture, by the painter in his picture, by the inventor in his invention, must be contained and organically represented in the innermost of his brain. The work of art, good or bad, cannot help being the translation of the law and order, or of the want of law and order, in the mental composition and organization of its creator. How, then, can the good fruit of rational imagination ever grow from a bad stock? Its essential condition must needs be a good stock well nourished and well trained.*

* An interesting exposition might, I think, be made of the characteristic features by which the epileptic imagination sometimes betrays itself in novels. A good example to select for the purpose of demonstration would be the Carthaginian romance *Salammbô* by Gustave Flaubert; the violent, abrupt, and exaggerated scenes and incidents of the book—so many enormities, if not monstrosities, of unbridled imagination

Having a true conception of the forming process of imagination one may survey the elaborate instincts of such little creatures as ants and bees with less wonder, perhaps with more understanding, than it has been the fashion to do. The puzzle will not seem so great why they do imagination's work without imagination. For that is what they virtually do. Although the ant does, on a small scale, the same kind of work which the bricklayer does on a large scale, there is said to be a vast difference, if not between the like works, at all events between the like workers, because the ant works by instinct and the bricklayer by mind. That is to play with words without settling what their value is, or whether they have value at all. It were wiser, putting the words aside, to go directly below them to the study of the things which they are used to denote and thought to explain and to try to get a clear apprehension of what they are.

Consider well what the Pelopœus wasp does. It collects clay in round pellets which it carries off in its mouth to build its nest, working with cheerful hum to place each pellet fitly on the edge of the cell, and to spread it out over the circular rim by means of the lower lip, guided by the mandible, itself astride over the rim the while. After the addition of every fresh pellet it takes a turn round, patting the side of the wall with its feet inside and outside, before flying off to gather another pellet. What essentially does the bricklayer do more? No doubt in the wasp's nervous system the power to do the clever work it does is innate or implanted or instinct—in other words, is in it; *that* is the necessary function of its organism constructed as it is, though it may still be that the creature learns some part of its skill by imitation of its kind. For in no creature, not even

---

delighting in the extraordinary, the outrageous, the impossible—doubtless being to the real characters and events of the Carthage they aspire to reproduce very much what epileptic convulsions are to the normal movements of a performing athlete.

in man, do we take adequate account of the part which instruction by imitation plays in making it what it is : the bird's song is not, any more than man's morality, entirely instinctive. However that be, it is certain that in the main intelligence is implicit in the wasp's structure, and that the individual never could learn its accomplishments in its lifetime; that we have in it a nervous mechanism able to perform an intelligent piece of work which, were it human work, would be thought certainly to denote the preordaining intelligence of mind. The silent intelligence shown by the wasp would be vastly greater in degree no doubt, but would not differ in kind, were it to build a cathedral for its cell.

The bricklayer's case is different, it may be said, because he learns consciously and does designedly what the wasp does instinctively and automatically. But is it quite certain that the wasp is entirely unconscious when it does so well work which, were it conscious, we should call intelligent and ascribe to reason ; making, as the manner is, the ordered proportion in the work—its *ratio* or reason, that is to say —a metaphysical faculty to do it? If it be so, then it is all the more easy to conceive that when the nervous system of man does like intelligent work the consciousness which attends the process is attendant only, an adjunct not essential to the working agent. Why should an intelligence which does not need to learn, but is perfect for its purpose, not be as good evidence of mind as an intelligence which has to be formed and perhaps works lamely in the end? If not of mind, what is the instinctive intelligence evidence of? To say that it is the work of instinct is nonsense, since it is the faculty which is instinct, not instinct which is a faculty. If the answer be, not of an insect-mind but of a supreme universal mind instinct in it, then it ought to be shown what else a mind so localized and conditioned in the insect is but the insect's mind, and what more a similarly localized and conditioned human mind is.

In any case it is indisputable that the exact and special reason incorporate in the insect's present nervous structure was not there from all eternity, but was somehow acquired and ingrafted, whether consciously or not, by ancestors in its line of organic development. All that the bricklayer does is to gain for himself in a less precise way and in a comparatively short time what the wasp owes to the precise gains of its kind made in past places through past ages. And that assuredly he could not do if he did not himself inherit, instinct in the present constitution of his nervous system, a large foundation of latent intelligence gained in the same way by labouring ancestors; more perhaps than he ever gains for himself consciously. Moreover, when he has by practice acquired the perfect skill to do a complex deed or to form an instant judgment he does it unconsciously and automatically, as the wasp does its building : the work is done by the fitly trained organic mechanism whether consciousness attends it or not, and done all the better the less the consciousness ; and it cannot be done, however keen and busy the consciousness, until the fit mechanism has been organized. The function is just the outward expression of the inward law of structural synthesis. In the result, then, the wasp and the bricklayer are in much the same case, though they stand on different planes of organic development; in both the nervous system does purposive work automatically. Manifestly, too, it is not quite lawful to say that the wasp knows not what it does, seeing that we know not what its consciousness may be ; nor that the man knows what he does, seeing that when his skill is perfect it is unconscious.

What then is the right conclusion? Not to put a metaphysical something into the one to do what the other does well without such an agent, but to see and own that nerve-structure itself, at certain heights and in certain forms of complex organization, can do of itself, and does as the necessary functional expression of its organized nature, such purposive acts as we mean by intelligent and suppose to need a pre-designing consciousness. What we christen intelligence or reason are the implicit laws of its structural organization when they become explicit in function; they are the definite mathematical proportions or ratios of such structuralized synthesis; and its implicit affinities and repulsions of elements, when they are explicit, are sympathies and antipathies, loves and hates. There is really nothing more nor less wonderful in the intelligence of the insect's instinct than of the man's reason, nothing more unwarrantable than to make an impassable chasm between them, nothing more gratuitous than to ascribe them to different suppositious entities. His intelligent admiration of its skill, what is it at bottom but the attesting sympathy of similar organic manufacture, the natural effect of connatural structure? From monad to man the continuity of nature is unbroken.

So paramount a creature as man may not allow that the humble intelligence which the nervous system of an ant performs can be of the same kind as the high intelligence which his brain performs; his superior dignity is instant to exact that his endowments shall differ not in degree only, but in kind. Nevertheless, if things are looked at simply and clearly as they are, without preconceived bias, still more striking examples of a community of nature between him and the animal world are manifest, not only in the manifold instinctive intelligences exhibited by different species of animals, but in the remarkable social developments which some of them have achieved. Imagine all these accomplishments, all these various examples of intelligent instinct and social union, now dispersed among different creatures, to be collected into one creature, harmonized there, and displayed by it in unity of function; the result would be a prodigy of varied intelligence which, if not of human height in all respects, albeit higher in some respects, would show something, rudimental or perfect, of every quality which man considers to

distinguish him mentally. How many thousands of
thousands of years elapsed before he could do in
whole what animals have done for innumerable ages
in distributed parts? His most vaunted inventions,
products of intellect which he can never sufficiently
admire and esteem himself for, often follow in the
wake of very ancient examples and do not always
overtake them. Why, then, cannot variety of
nervous organization, collected and concentrated in
him, do as a whole by itself what it confessedly does
in separate parts distributed through various animal
species?

Even moral feeling, which, being the attribute of
man's highest nature, he deems most markedly human
and esteems good enough to be of divine quality, is
found dispersed through different species of animals
and presents notable varieties in different individuals
of the same species. Take for example his next-of-
kin, the monkeys: they show the widest differences
of moral character, some being gentle, good-natured,
lively, and confiding; others morose, peevish, and
fretful; others obstinate, spiteful, and malicious.
The howling monkey of the Lower Amazons is sullen,
surly, and untameable, and does not survive many
weeks in captivity. The Caiarara monkey, which is
a most restless creature, though not playful like most
American monkeys, is easily made a pet of; yet
its disposition betokens a singular nervous irritability
and discontent; its expression of countenance is
anxious, painful, and changeable, and there is a want
of purpose and satisfaction in its restless movements;
it is not happy when it has got what it wants—*e.g.*,
its favourite food, a banana, but will leave it to snatch
morsels out of a companion's hand. In these moral
traits, in which it singularly resembles a variety of
human idiocy, it differs widely from its nearest
kindred, another common variety of which is much
quieter, better-tempered, and full of tricks that are
of a playful character. It is most certain that mere
nervous organization exhibits in these varied patterns

of temper and disposition very different moral qualities. And not in monkeys only, for different species of animals exhibit as many degrees and varieties of rudimentary moral feeling as might perhaps, if collected into one creature, abate the vaunt of human conceit.

When we consider truly the social life of ants, so perfect of its kind and so striking as a whole, it plainly appears that it has been the occasion of more unintelligent admiration than intelligent meditation. Counting social life essentially a human prerogative, men for the most part overlook what it really is and means in insects; it is as much as they do to give it the salute of a passing verbal acknowledgment. Yet in industry, in war, in plunder, in specialization of labour, in foresight, in diligence and discipline, in individual self-sacrifice to secure the greatest happiness of the greatest number, the ants have anticipated, if not exceeded, human co-operation; they have realized the socialistic ideal of a commonwealth which is wealth in common and established the most stable social system in the world.

In their social co-operation to the ends of a peaceful industrialism how completely is egoism swallowed up in altruism! The individual lives only for his kind; loves his neighbour as himself; dreams not of personal aggrandizement, not even of personal reproduction; cares only for the well-being and the immortality of the kind. A Comtist kneeling reverently before the Supreme Being of humanity, adoring its past progress, applauding its present strivings, discerning in its aspirations the blessed hope and promise of future progress to unimaginable heights, could hardly show or demand a more absolute reverence and devotion to his kind.

If such adoring worship of the kind by the ants be not religion—albeit it is of the essence of religion—or at all events not a religion of sufficient merit to be given the title, they will show superior and more abstract worship. A worship of the productive force in nature, not in gross phallic form practised by a low human kind, but in their pious devotion to the queen as the reproductive organ of the species : the sort of worship fundamentally which at a higher mental remove becomes the human worship of the sacred principle of motherhood.

Seeing how perfectly ants have realized the moral ideal of that peaceful industrialism which is proclaimed now to be the proper aim of human endeavour, it were a curious enquiry to make whether it is the destiny of a perfecting human society to reach at last a similar state of perfect ant-like social cooperation; a state in which immorality shall have no place, the categorical moral imperative ruling imperiously, since everybody will be instinctively or mechanically moral. A peace indeed which sexual passion, cause of so many woes to mankind, shall cease from troubling, because reproduction will be provided for in appointed social ways, not for the selfish and reckless gratification of the individual, but solely for the propagation of the kind; perhaps as among social insects by the selection of a number of breeders to be specially fed, groomed, cared for, and set apart for the purpose. As it is not to be supposed that ants were always in their present blessed state of peaceful social union, but on the contrary pretty certain that they went through much painful travail of transition to attain to it in the remote ages of developing ant-life on earth, we may be sure that their nervous system once possessed a plasticity which it no longer possesses now that it is set to its fixed and apparently final form : the plasticity was a necessary quality of the forming and perfecting organism, it is no longer a quality of the formed and perfected work. To stereotype the human kind in a like peaceful immobility must necessarily involve a like loss of nervous plasticity; and that will mean the suppression of those individual variations and their embodied impulses which disturb human society now, but its members fondly think make for progress. Though such an outlook of moral stagnation in perfected morality seem but flat and insipid, a somewhat dreary and monotonous prospect, still it may be that as ants have shown men the way of social life on earth they are ordained to show them also what is to be the end of it.

Observation and consideration of the ways of ants at all events prove that their nervous system contains implicitly theories of social life which man's reason does not invent, only sets forth expressly in knowledge. His mental superiority lies in knowing what he does and in learning to do more : he can make to himself conscious representations of that which in ants is direct reaction to immediate presentation, and use these representations advisedly to modify future reactions. This manifest superiority he manifestly owes to the superposition in his brain of a higher order of nervous tracts—those which constitute the organization of the cerebral cortex. It is in these supreme parts of the nervous hierarchy, which the ant is devoid of, that experiences are sorted, classified, stored, and duly labelled; it is the function of such structuralized proportion and order which we denominate intelligence and reason, they are the very laws of its vital composition and organization; and it is by virtue of such superior structure and function that man has the superior order of mind enabling him to reflect on what he does, and to exult over the mean ant which has it not. But it is to go clean contrary to the teachings of sense and reason, and to ignore the positive evidence of experiment and experience, to assume that the higher order of nervous organization has no functions of its own, and cannot of itself perform rational or proportional functions implicit in its structure; and it is gratuitous to assign it and to insist it must have metaphysical help to do the kind of work which a lower order of nervous organization does in simpler fashion instinctively.

Cleverly as ants work together in society to do skilful work, it is not likely that they ever consciously imagine what they go to do. Not in one of the

different senses in which the term imagination is
loosely used : not the conscious imaging of a past
event which is often called imagination, though it is
more properly memory; nor the imaging or picturing
to mind of an event to be, such as a dog may have
when it is in eager pursuit of the scent of a hare which
it expects every instant to see start in front of it;
least of all, the productive or creative imagination
which marks the highest power of the function, and
only the best minds are capable of. There is plainly
no imagination of the end, no conscious purpose, in
the purposive reflex action : the eyelid does not think
what it does when it winks to protect the eye. Nor
is there imagination in purely instinctive action : the
calf does not mentally foresee when, after staggering
clumsily to its feet, it gets blundering hold of its
mother's pap and sucks it. But it is nowise so
certain that there is no sort of imagination in a
dog's play. The performances of a dog at play are
notably either mimic-chase, or mimic-battle, or
mimic-love; and all its eager snuffing and scenting
when it is busily running to and fro along the road
have reference either to creatures of a kind which it
likes to pursue, or to creatures of its own kind whose
traces it likes to perceive. Has it not then some
kind of mental image of what its senses are so busily
interested in? Are its actions nothing more than
directly reflex?

The fact that a dog dreams and barks in its dream
shows pretty plainly that it can form some mental
images, as also do the positive hallucinations which it
undoubtedly has when, gone mad, it bites savagely at
friends and phantoms. Its considerable capacity of
learning accomplishments, and the definite expectations which it may be taught to entertain—accomplishments and expectations answering instantly and
exactly to their proper and, perhaps, nicely differenced
signs—point to the same conclusion. If a ball be
thrown forward high in the air a dog used to the play
rushes forward the instant it sees the proper motion

of throwing, and catches the ball on the bound; if, feigning to throw the ball forward as usual, the thrower trickily throws it behind him it rushes forward as before in expectation to see it drop, and, deceived, is all abroad at first; soon, however, it detects the trick which has been played it, and, watching more closely the precise manner of throwing, rushes backwards or forwards as the case requires. Therein it reasons and expects, not otherwise, though better, than the person does who having spilt salt on the table-cloth and found misfortune follow, expects to the day of his death bad luck whenever he or anyone else spills salt; but it soon does what he probably never does, it observes attentively the exact sequences of events and corrects the erroneous expectation. Is the wrong reasoning of human superstition evidence of mind, and the right reasoning of canine intelligence evidence of no mind? Yet the strange thing to see is that the mortal who hugs his superstition based on bad reasoning will be said commonly to give proof therein of imagination, whereas the animal which corrects a wrong and forms a right imagination by sound reasoning will be refused imagination and reason. The truth is that it is much the fashion to think imagination all that, and only that, which it does when it is divorced from reason, and to see its highest flights in the vain things which it imagines when most divorced from reason.

So long as imagination is reckoned an entity which does this or that in mental function, instead of being viewed as the function of a cerebral process which may be of all kinds and degrees of activity, so long will an absolute barrier in theory, which exists not in fact, be kept up between animal and human mind, and so long will the animal be denied mental functions which it gives as good evidence of possessing as the lowest specimens of mankind. For of them it may certainly be said that their imagination does not go much beyond that sort of concrete imaging which is the memory of what has been before, projected into the expectation of what will be; the memory-inspired expectation of the old hunter which, hearing the distant cry of the hounds in pursuit of the fox, when it is trotting quietly along the road, is instantly excited and restive, looking eagerly round to see the chase appear and to start off with it.

What in any case is perplexing to those who cannot think that the proper function of the brain is to perform intelligence, who wonder, therefore, that it is not entirely inert mentally when consciousness is in abeyance, is the remarkable work which it does in dreams. That dream-dramas should have the vividness they have is not surprising, seeing that they engage the stage and the light exclusively; but why they should have the inventive fertility, the wonderful variety, the grotesque compositions, the incongruous mixtures of events, the illogical logic they have usually, yet for all that from time to time a perfect congruity and coherence of events, passes present explanation. It is beyond question that the mind can do as good work in dreams as it ever does when awake—indeed, better imaginative work; a person will reason then sometimes quite logically, construct and judge rightly individual character, ascribing the fit action to it in events and the fit language in dialogue, put to himself sensible questions and receive apt replies, make speeches which he finds perfectly coherent when he wakes, solve mathematical problems correctly, compose poetry which is not nonsense, invent riddles and answer them. Nobody alleges that a predesigning consciousness then goes before the imaginative work; the brain, started on a right track of function, obeys the laws of correct mental synthesis incorporate in it by nature and training. It is a striking exemplification of the real conditions of its working in the conscious function which we call imagination and thereupon imagine *an* or *the* imagination in order to perform. No doubt such coherent mental function is exceptional in dreams, albeit not more so perhaps than coherent thinking by day in most minds outside the ruts of habit, dreams generally being examples of very irregular mental compositions; not otherwise than as if chemical elements (crude though the comparison be), instead of combining according to their regular laws in proper compounds, were to go wild dances adrift into all sorts of irregular random and unstable fugitive compounds. Were the exact properties of the organic elements of the brain, their affinities and repulsions, their laws of composition and disposition, and all about their workings known as well as the properties and laws of combination of chemical elements are known, it might be possible to detect scraps or fragments of method, a kind of order of disorder, in the phantasmagoria of dreams; but the whole business is yet too complex and obscure to admit of even partial exposition.

Meanwhile dreams may yield some useful hints with respect to the working of imagination. The first reflection to suggest itself is that the imagination which works coherently in dreaming is imagination well trained by good observation and reflection in waking life. The foolish imagination will not be wise in dreams : how can the structural syntheses of faulty components be perfect ? The good fruit, when it chances, is nowise a gift of inspiration to weak minds during sleep; it is the natural production of a strong mind on lines of function in respect of which its ordinary thought is coherent and rational. Such habitually steady reflection being rare, since the daily imaginations of most minds are hardly less incoherent, fantastic, and futile than the imaginations of their dreams, the marvel would be if they ever did chance to dream soberly and sanely—if unruly imaginations then followed right rules. What, then, is the moral for the waking imagination ? That it can work soundly only when it has been so steadily and sanely informed by right observation and reason as to mature in silent gestation the offspring which in due season it brings forth into conscious light.

Another truth which dreams exemplify is the spontaneity and exceeding activity of imagination, whereby it comes to pass infallibly that, if not set and kept to orderly work, it runs riot in disorderly work. That it may be allowed to do in play if its ramblings, when it thus gambols, are appraised after their kind—that is, as wanton exercises of play, not serious things.

Lastly, in the character and composition of dreams one may take note of the same factors that work in waking imagination to determine the forms of the composition. The present mood of mind manifestly counts for much, whether it be due to internal bodily causes or to external moral causes; for it inspires the tone of feeling directly, and thus acts indirectly to summon and marshal the forms and combinations of characters and events that sort with it. Also the natural temper of the individual mind fails not to manifest itself in the character of the created drama; an impetuous nature is not meek nor a meek nature impetuous in the various scenes of it. And again, the unexhausted effects of the recent experiences of the day, whether conscious, barely conscious, or unconscious experience, frequently prove their latent activity by the part they take in dreams of the night; for, although some impressions seem to be unnoticed at the time or, if noticed, forgotten immediately afterwards, yet their stimulated nerve-tracts retain an irritability or sub-conscious activity which disposes them to enter easily again into conscious activity. Such dream-instances go to show how essentially character, temper, and experience, recent and remote, enter into the working of waking imagination.

The one broad fact which dreams strongly exemplify is the plastic power of the brain to work up the materials of experience, whether old experience incorporate in structure or recent functional experience, into new mental compositions—to perform, in fact, synthetic or so-called imaginative work of the most varied character. That these productions are usually fantastic and absurd is no matter; what else could be expected, seeing that the conditions under which the brain works in sleep exclude the constant impressions on sense from the surroundings and the habitual associations of ideas which do so much to hold the waking brain to definite tracts of activity and preclude nearly all other activity in many brains? However monstrous and incongruous the products, they are still natural; the effects and evidence of laws of composition gone astray in disorder. That we cannot tell how and why they have gone wrong is proof only that we do not yet understand them, not proof that they will not be understood some day.

Let the theory of mind be what it may, it is certain that its function of imagination rests on an organic process which is not of different order of being from other organic processes.

PART II

UNSOUND MENTAL ACTION

CHAPTER I

MENTAL MALFORMITIES

To run a distinct line of division between sound and
unsound mental functions, however much to be wished
in theory, is impossible in fact, since there are intermediate states of development and disorder making
an unbroken gradation from the sanest to the insanest
thought and feeling. Mental pathologists have not
taken due account of this truth in their studies of
morbid psychology, though they have not entirely
overlooked it. Their business being to treat insanity
of mind as disease or madness, they have not concerned themselves with the instances in which it is
not disease in the proper sense of the word, but
irregular and defective function—deformity rather
than derangement of intellect; not organic machinery
in disorder, but organic machinery of bad order of
construction and function.

It is from no want of obtrusive self-assertion that
such instances are neglected; for while malformities
of body, being simply disabling, are fitted to excite
compassion in others, malformities of mind are often
such active causes of trouble and annoyance in the
world that they provoke anger and contempt. A
person of lame body, knowing his infirmity, or at all
events knowing it to be no superiority, probably tries
to hide it; but a person of lame mind is so far from
knowing his infirmity that he commonly esteems
himself above those who are well formed mentally,
and thrusts it forwards.

There is a large class of peculiar persons much
differing from one another, who, agreeing in being

unlike the majority of people of their age and country
in their modes of thought, feeling, and action, have
their several tendencies to deviation from the common
nature described as eccentricity; instead of moving
in the common orbits of human thought and feeling,
they evince impulses to start from them—are eccentric. All insane persons are eccentric, but all eccentric
persons are not insane. From a practical point of
view any one may be permitted to be as eccentric as
he pleases, to go as much as he likes off the beaten
track of thinking, feeling, and doing, so long as his
deviations or vagaries do not compromise social order;
but there is a point of nonconformity at which the
body social must interfere to protect itself if it is
to continue in well-being. Unbounded licence for
erratic individuals to do as they like would be incompatible with the holding together of the framework
of the special society. From another point of view
eccentricities of thought and conduct have their
curious interest, inasmuch as from time to time they
turn out to be mental variations that initiate new
and useful developments; rarely and exceptionally,
no doubt, but still here and there, and now and then.

It is proper to note that special sensibilities with
singular talents of thought or performance in particular departments of knowledge or art go along
sometimes with signal eccentricities; an extraordinary
development of one part of the mind being compatible
with a deformed or very defective condition of other
parts of it, however awkwardly the fact may conflict
with metaphysical notions of mind as something
which, having spiritual unity, has not extension or
parts and cannot be divided. Moreover, a shallow
intensity of temperament whereby a narrow notion is
hugged with exclusive fervour, without regard to
limitations and qualifications, and pushed with acrid
energy, without regard to occasions and hindrances,
is sometimes a useful practical force in the world, as
I have already pointed out. To see an aim clearly
and distinctly from a special standpoint, to feel no

distrust of it because it is a deviation from received opinion, to have the mind so engrossed by it as to be insensible to the ridicule and opposition which it encounters on all hands, is an excellent thing when the notion has truth and life in it. The spectacle, at all events, is a redeeming exception to the servile conformity which is the habit of the multitude's mind.

But it ought to be well understood that a person of such quality of thinking and acting is constitutionally incapable of weighing evidence, that he perpetrates habitually almost all the faults of bad observation and reasoning which it is possible to perpetrate, and that the quality, in extreme degree, is the fanatical note of madness. When he is right it is not his merit, since it is not by virtue of right observation and reasoning on his part; it is a lucky peradventure, the happy fortune of his nature and circumstances. Owing to his exclusive intensity of thought and feeling, such a one is especially liable to positive hallucinations and illusions; his fervour not only transforming real impressions into the shapes of his imagination, but transporting his mental images into objective forms.

Most often a person of that quality of temperament is not right but wrong, or at any rate more wrong than right. Leaving positively insane persons out of account, the people who run into the exaggerated development of one idea, or are affected with a passionate wry-mindedness of one sort of another, or go askew in eccentric impulses of feeling and conduct, occasion a great deal of annoyance and suffering, and commonly do more harm than good in the world. It falls on others of a more wholesome and temperate wholeness of nature to make social atonement for them—to suffer for their self-indulgences, to thwart their follies, to counteract their extravagances, to smooth their difficulties, to rectify the disorders which they produce in the social body. They, meanwhile, absorbed in the narrow selfishness of their one-sided or wry-minded natures, care not sincerely for any aim except so far as it serves to gratify the modes of egoistic righteousness in which their intense and special self-love masquerades. Nevertheless, by the very intensity of their self-confidence, by their constitutional insensibility to other interests, by their fanatical zeal and singleness of purpose, they sometimes get credit for their pretensions and attract followers who look up to them as semi-inspired.

Thus it has been that religious impostors have arisen and flourished. Not consciously insincere at the outset, perhaps, they have first deceived themselves, then imposed upon others, and in the end, by the reflex effect upon themselves of the admiration and reverence of which they were the objects, have become more or less conscious impostors, affecting the sanctity and inspiration which their disciples ascribe to them. Wanting in intellectual wholeness and sincerity by reason of a natural flaw of mental structure, it is inevitable that they become morally insincere. They delude others for their own gain or glory; and to delude others is a sure way to become, by a stealthy process of self-collusion, self-deluded. It is signal unreason to challenge authority and reverence for a person of this sort, tacitly or expressly, because of his burning zeal and sincerity, since he may be as little capable of correct observation, as incapable of self-observation, and as deeply sunk in self, as if he were actually insane. To christen a vice zeal is not to transform it into a virtue. His nature is not well tempered, it is intemperate, and on the way, therefore, to becoming distempered; and in any case the quality of its sincerity is very poor, for the sincerest person to self, albeit the insincerest to nature all round, is the lunatic.

The mind is not a single function or faculty, uncompounded and working always in the same simplicity and unity; it is a federation of functions or faculties which, having their divers subordinate operations and interests, are bound together into the organic unity of the whole. As the body, being

a confederation of many different organs and structures, has its organic unity, whereby all parts work
together in fellowship to one end, the whole in each
part and each part in the whole; so the brain has its
unity, as the central co-ordinating organ in which all
parts of the body, directly or indirectly represented
in it, are brought into relations of action and reaction,
through the senses and movements, with the external
world : a multiplicity in unity, its unity being a
compound resultant of many parts and functions.
Now it is impossible to develop one leading function or
one class of functions to excess without doing so at the
expense of other functions and to its own detriment;
the hypertrophy of it is the inevitable atrophy of them.

The intermediate borderland of thought and
feeling between soundness and unsoundness of mind,
being penumbral, has been thickly peopled with
supernatural beings. It is less populous now than
once it was, because, like other enchanted regions, it
has been partially surveyed and taken possession of
by positive knowledge, but it is still not barren of
wonders. Ghost-seers and ghost-seekers are to be
met with, in such numbers and of such zeal, too, in
England as to have formed a society for the systematic
prosecution of their researches; and they look com-
passionately down from their superior spiritual
heights on the inferior mental qualities of those
devoid of their fine spiritual sense. Great indeed
will be their reward if it be that which they joyfully
anticipate—to wit, the proof of the reality of the
spiritual world by material evidence, the demonstration of the supernatural by natural means, the
vision of the soul by the eye of the body.

Without endorsing the observations of enthusiasts,
who are often signally disqualified by frame and
temper of mind from observing accurately at all, and
signally qualified to embrace eagerly that which suits
their neurotic strain, this much reason may fairly be
granted to those who seek for sensible evidence of
supersensible things : first, that matter undoubtedly

exists in so fine, subtle, and, so to speak, spiritualized a state as to be imperceptible to human sense, and in that condition is amazingly active; secondly, that, though we cannot then perceive it by sense, it is possible we may nevertheless be affected powerfully by it. To leap, however, from this confession to the creation of a world of spiritual beings of human kind and form is to try to go forwards by going backwards —it is to seek for the material and forms of perfecting in defective observation and thought; for certainly there has been no new discovery of laws and properties of matter in these latter days to warrant the least belief that it ever takes the invisible form and substance of a ghost.

The belief is really a reversion to the old belief of ignorant folk among whom spirits and ghosts abounded; an example of the revival or recrudescence of a still-surviving superstition, not a new conquest of scientific thought; and the method of thought pursued is none other than the old method which filled nature with spirits in the past, making the counterfeit of knowledge where no knowledge was. To think of spirit as a name for the most subtle manifestations of material substance has a seeming savour of science, seeing that, however much men may subtilize and refine matter, they who owe all the material and forms of their ideas to sensory perception cannot immaterialize it entirely, cannot really conceive spiritual existence or agency save as endowed with some of its properties; but it is signal inconsistency thereupon to make grossly sensible to eye in ghost form, or palpable to touch by a spirit-hand, or audible to ear, a material agency the essential character of which is a tenuity too fine for the appreciation of sense. Though it be allowable to transcend reason by faith in the domain of religion, since it is the fundamental postulate of religious faith to exalt the foolishness of the simple above the wisdom of the wise, it is still not lawful and right to stultify reason in its own province of natural knowledge.

CHAPTER II

HALLUCINATIONS AND ILLUSIONS

THAT many theories of the supernatural have had their origin and sustenance in the operations of disordered mind cannot be disputed by anyone whose knowledge entitles him to have and express an opinion on the subject. Of these disordered operations of mind the most striking outcomes notably are Hallucinations and Illusions, Mania and Delusions. Their nature, origin, and significance I go on now to consider briefly and summarize compendiously.

By hallucination is meant such a false perception of sense as a person has when he sees, hears, touches, or otherwise apprehends as external, that which has no existence at all outside his consciousness, no objective basis—sees a person where there is no person, hears a voice where there is no voice, feels a touch when he is not touched. It is the creation of a fitting outward impression as cause of a special sensation where the impression is not made; and it takes place in accordance with the well-known physiological law that it is possible, by stimulating artificially the trained nerve-centres of perception, to produce the same kind of perception, and quite as vividly, as the natural stimulus of the proper external object produces. When there is an external object to excite the perception, but the nature of it is mistaken (far the most common case), it is usual and useful to describe the effect as illusion, although it is not possible in nature to draw a distinct line always between hallucination and illusion.

Obviously a person may have both hallucination and illusion without derangement of the understanding; but the false perception is then commonly a transitory event which he is able to appreciate and correct by suitable experience. No one has any difficulty in recognizing the internal origin of the flash of light which he perceives after a smart blow on his eye, and he who hears a roaring noise in his ears after hanging his head low down knows very well that the cause of the sound is not outside himself. But if the impact and force of a blow were so exactly limited and so nicely measured as just to produce the special perception of a special sense and no more, he could hardly then help believing in its temporary reality.

These examples illustrate one cause and mode of production of hallucinations—namely, a disturbance or disorder of the special nerve-centres of perception. It is of no present concern whether that disturbance be a direct molecular commotion of their nerve-elements or the secondary effect of a disordered supply or quality of the blood by which their structure is nourished. The disturbance being temporary, the hallucinations disappear with its disappearance. In deeper and more lasting brain-disorders a similar cause produces more decided and lasting hallucinations. For example, when the mind of the fever-stricken patient begins to wander he sees among the familiar faces around him the visions of strange faces which he knows at first are not real faces, only phantom-faces, though they are as vivid as real faces; perhaps they appear only when his eyes are shut or when the room is dark, and vanish when he opens his eyes or when the room is lit up. After a little while they are more frequent, persisting when his eyes are open and in broad daylight, so that he gets perplexed and uncertain about their reality; assents, perhaps, for the moment when assured that they are phantoms, but falls back instantly into troubled doubt. At last they get entire mastery of his belief, all uncertainty vanishes, and, distinguishing not between them and real figures, he talks to them as real persons. He is now delirious or insane.

In the delirium of insanity it is a common thing for

the sufferer to see and hear persons who are the mere phantom-creations of his disordered brain. When the delirium is acute these are so vivid and active, so dominate his senses and usurp his attention, that real persons and voices can make no true impression upon him; his mind is then cut off from the actual world by the very intensity of a turbulent activity which, inhibiting the true functions of the senses, so deranges their communications that the eye seeing sees not, the ear hearing hears not, and the touch touching feels not; like a person in a nightmare, he lives in a tumultuous ideal world, which has all or more than all the vividness of the things of the real world. When the delirium is limited, as it is sometimes when the malady is chronic, he is haunted by one or two special hallucinations which cling to him in spite of the opposing evidence of facts, albeit that, apart from them, he is capable of receiving and appreciating rightly the impressions made upon his senses. Nothing is more remarkable sometimes than the entire credence yielded to a false perception almost or quite impossible in the nature of things, and certainly of inherent absurdity in the common judgment of all the rest of the world, by one who in most other respects seems to be in possession of his senses and reason. But when he is under its dominion he is not in possession of them, for its morbid activity excludes their sane influence and possesses him.

It is easy enough to demonstrate the physical causation of hallucinations, for they can be produced artificially by suitable vitiation of the blood. If anyone swallows a poisonous dose of belladonna, he falls into a state of unquiet and busy delirium in which he sees before him unreal persons to whom he chatters and unreal objects at which he stares and grasps, and is restlessly engaged in unreal trans-actions; all these juggles of the brain disappearing and he returning to his right senses when the poison which, circulating in it, deranges its functions, is removed from the body by the organs of excretion.

D

He has not the least doubt of the objective reality of the visionary objects so long as he is under its influence; he has not the least doubt of their entirely visionary nature so soon as he is freed from its poisonous effects. The tainted thought bespeaks the tainted blood.

A frequent co-operating factor in this production of hallucinations by direct disturbance of the nerve-centres of perception, of which due account should be taken, is a native bent of the centres themselves to irregular action : they tend to what they end in. It was noticed how in fever the reason at first resisted the hallucinations—as sane life always reacts to defend or save itself from threatened hurt—and only afterwards, as the disorder augmented, succumbed to them. Although the strongest reason could not withstand the invasion if the physical commotion were great enough, yet there is no doubt that brains differ much in natural stability, possessing different native powers of resistance to shocks, and that some brains fall into delirium from causes which would not disturb others so deeply. Now, it is in those that have an innate trend to irregular function, owing to a predisposition to insanity, epilepsy, or allied nervous disorder, that the confederate centres, being more loosely bound together and more prone to act separately, are more likely to suffer dissolution of function. Where co-order is weak, disorder is easy. Then a slight cause may suffice to produce delirium— for example, a moderate fever, or a strain of emotion, or a pressure of overwork, or some other cause which would do no serious hurt to a strong brain whose centres were stably organized. Moral causes of madness mostly mean fault in the mental fabric.

It has been a belief almost as old as the hills and as widespread as mankind that abnormal and morbid nervous states had a supernatural significance : that some deity or demon was at work in them. Among the ancients epilepsy was a sacred disease; it was thought to have something divine in it, as it

and madness are still thought by Eastern nations to
have. Its sudden and overwhelming invasion; the
violence with which the whole body was instantly
precipitated into convulsions, as if fearfully shaken
by a demon that had taken possession of it or whose
possession it was convulsively labouring to repel;
the trance-like unconsciousness of the sufferer during
the appalling commotion and the occasional muttering
of incoherent sentences by him—these were sufficient
to give it the appearance and credit of a supernatural seizure.*

Another reason for this opinion doubtless was the
vivid hallucinations which frequently go along with
the seizures. If it be the hearing that is affected, a
voice is heard with startling distinctness to utter
threat, or command, or admonition; if it be a
hallucination of vision, a figure or face is seen illu-
minated by a bright or coloured halo of light produced,
like it, by the disturbed centres of perception; if it
be the muscular sense which is troubled, there may be
the bewildering feeling of the rising of the body into
the air or of its sinking into the ground.† When
the person comes to himself the strange and startling
experience of sense continues so to vibrate in his
memory as to keep up the vivid impression for a time;
and as he is utterly unable to account to himself for
its mysterious origin he is the more disposed to
believe that he really saw or heard an angel from
heaven, or had a visit from the Holy Ghost, or was
carried up into heaven or down into hell. That
some angelic apparitions and heavenly visions had
this kind of origin is most certain.

* " Master, I have brought unto thee my son which hath
a dumb spirit; and wheresoever it taketh him, it dasheth
him down : and he foameth, and grindeth his teeth, and
pineth away . . .: and when he saw him, straightway the
spirit tare him grievously; and he fell on the ground, and
wallowed foaming." (Mark ix. 17–20, Revised Version.)
† " You see and feel it," says St. Theresa, " as a cloud,
or a strong eagle rising upwards and carrying you away on
its wings."

In every large lunatic asylum at the present day
are to be found epileptics who are subject to similar
hallucinations in connection with their fits : vain
and good-humoured often when they are free from
fits, but arrogant, irritable, suspicious, and aggressive
when they suffer in connection with them, they
evince delusions of being Jesus Christ or some other
great personage of Scripture, or of having received
revelations from one or another of these personages.
Dangerous beings, too, they sometimes are, because
of their hallucinations.

If the tradition be true that Mahomet was epileptic,
the visions which he had during so-called swoons
may well have had an epileptic origin. The great
change of character which he underwent and the
prophetic mission which he undertook, whatever their
real inspiration, followed an extraordinary vision
and extreme mental commotion. The story is that,
as he walked in solitary meditation in a lonely valley
near Mecca, he was greeted suddenly with the words,
" Hail to thee, O messenger of God ! " On looking
to the right hand and to the left to see whence the
voice came, he saw nothing but stones and trees.
It was soon afterwards that the angel Gabriel appeared
to him in a vision on Mount Hira and delivered to him
the message of God of which he was chosen to be the
prophet. Great was his trouble of mind, however,
after this visitation, so great that he went in anxious
distress to Kadijah, his wife, fearing that he was
possessed ; and, although she comforted and reassured
him, his mental agony in the subsequent conflict
of feelings was such that he was several times tempted
to end his life by throwing himself off Mount Hira.
Was the vision, then, after all, the vision, and the
voice the voice, of an epileptic trance ?

The pious Mussulman will naturally repudiate this
natural explanation of what he believes to have been
a supernatural event, but the Christian will still think
it the charitable interpretation of what he must else
rank as imposture ; biased to the worse interpreta-

tion by the knowledge of how much fraud holy Mahdis in the East are wont to mix with their prophetic pretensions. But in what light will the devout Mahometan view the miraculous vision by which Saul, the fiery persecutor of the disciples of Jesus, was converted from breathing threatenings and slaughters against them into the impassioned apostle and sagacious organizer of Christianity? The devout Christian may resent the impious insult of a natural explanation of a miraculous event; but how can the Mahometan, whose understanding is not overawed by fit faith into a devout belief of the incredible, be expected to exhibit a similar unquestioning credence? The stultification of reason which is truth to one is still nonsense to another religion.

These illustrations, if they have the character ascribed to them, are so eminent and significant as to render other illustrations, which would be weak by comparison, unnecessary. But many such are not wanting. Ann Lee, founder of the so-called Shakers, is said to have been epileptic; she had visions of the Saviour, who "became one with her in body and spirit." The apostle of the so-called Church of the New Jerusalem, Emanuel Swedenborg, who professed to be in daily intercourse with angels and to receive revelations from them, was subject at one time of his life to seizures which were closely akin to, if they were not actually, epilepsy. The Siberian schamans or medicine-men who pretend to intercourse with invisible powers and with the spirits of the dead, working themselves, like the priestesses of the ancient oracle of Delphi, into a state of frenzy in which they foam at the mouth and are convulsed, always select by preference for pupils of their mysteries boys who are subject to epileptic attacks. When the breath of inspiration came upon the Delphic priestess, she cried out, "Behold the god! behold the god!" and immediately fell backward in convulsive struggles, foaming at the mouth and prophesying. Among the Patagonians the magicians were chosen from persons seized with falling sickness or St. Vitus's dance; they were nervous and excitable men who, in uttering oracles, fell into actual convulsions.

Thus it appears clearly that in all peoples and parts of the world persons subject to epilepsy or like convulsive seizures have, by natural selection, come conspicuously to the front as the favourite organs, the most fit instruments, of supernatural inspirations. The epileptic temperament itself, apart from its ordinary conclusive incidents, seems specially propitious to that all-absorbing enthusiasm in which the mind, rapt from itself in a sort of ecstasy or exaltation of its whole energies, creates hallucinations and breeds the conceit of a divine inflation or possession.

Another condition of things favourable to the generation of hallucinations is severe exhaustion of brain, whether owing to mental or to bodily causes. The shipwrecked sailor, when delirious from long privation of food and drink, has various hallucinations, among others sometimes tantalizing dreams and visions of food and water, which are the illusive creations of his urgent needs. The long fastings, the scourgings, the exposure to extreme heat and cold, and the other mortifications of the body practised by the religious ascetic, who, fleeing from the society of his kind to some desert solitude, passed a lonely life in meditation, prayers, and penances, brought his monotonously and specially exercised brain to such an isolation from the ordinary and wholesome impressions of sense, and to such a state of irritable and spasmodic weakness, that he frequently saw visions which, according to his moods of feeling, were visions of angels who consoled him in his sufferings, or visions of devils who tempted and tormented him. Of such brain-sick kind were the temptations of St. Anthony and other saints, who, in order to subdue the besetting lusts of flesh, inflicted on themselves the extremest mortifications which a perverse ingenuity could devise : the visions which they obtained in consequence were no better than the juggles of starved brains. A Mahometan receipt in successful use at the present day for summoning spirits is to fast seven days in a lonely place, burning such incense as benzoin, aloe-wood, mastic, and other odoriferous wood from the Soudan, and to read a chapter from the Koran a thousand and one times in the seven days. The entire solitude, the long fasting, the monotonous exercise of uninterested attention, the stimulation of the exhausted and irritable brain by the aromatic and acrid vapours, have such an effect in due course that drums are beaten, flags hoisted, and spirits seen full of light and of beautiful and benign aspect.

Again we are in face of a general fact of pregnant significance : that in all places and in all times abnormal states of the nervous system, morbid and artificial, in which sense is thralled in ecstasy, have been esteemed ways of communication with the supernatural.

It happens now and then that sick persons on their death-beds see visions which are sometimes of a joyful, more often of an indifferent, occasionally of an appalling character. This experience, which is not limited to any country or time, or to the votaries of any religion, has most often befallen, not when death by acute disease or accident was an abrupt event, but when death by wasting disease was the gradual ending of mortality. Consumptive persons, owing to their slow decay of strength and to the frequent persistence of an irritable nervous animation even to the last, seem most liable to these death-bed visions ; accordingly, many of the telling scenes that make solemn impressions on those who witness and relate them, or more often relate them as witnesses without having witnessed them, occur in deaths from this wasting disease. As the brain-functions flicker before they expire, long-forgotten scenes and faces of the past, far-off events of childhood and youth which seemed lost in oblivion, arise unbidden in memory with startling vividness and are seen as

transient visions. The last word of the dying mother
is perhaps to utter the name of her long dead child
whose face she suddenly sees; the last act of the
expiring old man to start at the sight of his mother's
face as it was bent lovingly over him in childhood.
The physical shock of the very instant of death
unlocking silent memories of the brain, may be the
abrupt occasion of such hallucinations.

How easy, then, to wish, and, wishing, to hope, and
hoping, to believe, that in that supreme and solemn
moment is granted a fore-glimpse into the world of
spirits which is just about to open!—that as the
material grossness of earth falls away the nearly
emancipated spirit, hovering on the brink of a new
life, its vision purged of earthly dross, reaches such a
state of rarefaction, exaltation, and detachment as
to enjoy momentary access to the supernatural world.
Those who believe so, and base on the belief the pledge
and proof of a future life, ought to call to mind and
ponder well this fact—that the fever-stricken savage,
when abandoned to die by his companions, if he chances
to recover unexpectedly and rejoin them, sometimes
recounts the particulars of his visit to the world of
spirits during the crisis of his disease, telling a detailed
story of doings of his dead relatives there much like
their gross doings when on earth.

The sober question, of course, is whether, during the
final decay of faculties in the last stage of mental
and physical prostration, when life flickers in its ashes
and the dying person is capable of only a few signs
of feeble animation, there is suddenly opened in him
a power and kind of insight the like of which he never
had when he was strong and well. Is it lawful to
base on the expiring energies of a brain which " doth
by the feeble comments that it makes foretell the
ending of mortality " the momentous conclusion of
living beings in a supernatural world? If it be,
then the necessary conclusion is that all the insight
of man when he is in full vigour of mind and body
and all the knowledge which he has painfully accumu-

lated through the natural avenues of sense, are products of a method of observation and reflection which has no voucher of lasting validity, but, being of provisional value only, may be discredited and supplanted at any moment by the sudden opening of a special spiritual vision ; and the further conclusion may follow that this sort of vision, contrary to all natural experience, will be at its best when life is at its worst, the soundest mind be displayed in the unsoundest body.

CHAPTER III

HALLUCINATIONS AND ILLUSIONS—*continued*

THE foregoing examples of hallucinations illustrate their mode of origin in direct disturbance of the senses or of their sensory nerve-centres or tracks; originating there they then impose themselves upon belief. It now remains to consider the mode of origin of hallucination in the reverse order—namely, in a vividly conceived notion or belief which imposes itself upon sense. For the senses and reason reciprocally trick one another; and, as the senses present subjective impressions as objective and deceive thought, so thought in turn sometimes subjugates the senses, compelling them to perceive purely internal impressions as external objects.

Here I may call to mind what was previously said concerning the nature of ordinary perception : how that in each perception a person for the most part sees only a very small part of that which he thinks he sees, the mind contributing from the stock of its former experience what is necessary to fill up the image. The visual impression is never more than a sign to which experience has taught him to give its proper meaning—a sign which, without the complementary contributions of the instructed mind, would be meaningless, just as a written or spoken word of foreign language is meaningless to one who has not been instructed what to mean by it.

Here is manifest an easy opening for illusion and the source of one of the most common causes of erroneous observation. The active idea in the mind, if it fit not the perception, dominates and thus prevents true perception by forestalling it; and it is evident that a subjective activity of the kind, short of the degree necessary to cause actual hallucination, will suffice to cause illusion and error. Only by the test of actual experience can it be proved to be ungrounded, or not well grounded, in reality—proved, that is to say, to be a promise of reality which cannot be met, or met adequately, by payment on demand.

A proved efficient cause of hallucination, then, is a vividly conceived idea, so intense and so isolated thereby from transmission of its energy along the tracks of other ideas in reflection that it is projected outwards into what seems an actual perception—in the case of sight, for example, a mental image so vivid as to become a visual image; in the case of hearing, an idea so vivid as to become a voice.

The traditional habit of separating mind from body by an impassable chasm of origin, nature, and destiny leads to an ever-recurring astonishment at striking instances of the workings of mind in bodily processes as if the instances were singular, outside the usual order of nature, to be wondered at strangely. There is nothing more wonderful in the mind's action on the body than in the heart's action on the individual's feelings of warmth or well-being, such operations of it being as natural, constant, and necessary as any other physiological process : not an organic motion which does not help to make a mood, not a mood which does not affect an organic process. Here, as elsewhere, wonder, craning at extraordinary, takes no note of ordinary, instances.

How many times and to how many persons has it happened to discover that the vivid expectation of pain on moving a rheumatic muscle intensifies the pain when the movement is made ; which may indeed be made sometimes without any pain at all when the attention is distracted from it? Yet how little has the physiological lesson of the familiar fact, no less instructive than a thousand more striking facts of the same sort, been marked and appreciated. Set sense on the attentive bent, and it is inevitably more quick to feel, and feels more keenly, the impression which it awaits. It is within every one's experience that the keenly expectant idea of a particular sensation in a part of the body suffices sometimes to cause the sensation; and there are persons who, going further than that, can see or feel what they conceive vividly.

Sir Isaac Newton said of himself that he could at any time call up a spectrum of the sun in the dark by intense direction of his mind to the idea, " as when a man looks earnestly to see a thing which is difficult to be seen." Goethe had a similar power of making certain mental images sensible to sight, as some persons have habitually; and the great French novelist, Balzac, alleged that when he wrote the story of the poisoning of one of the characters in his novel by arsenic he had so distinct a taste of arsenic in his mouth afterwards that he was himself poisoned and vomited his dinner.* All the more instructive and effective proof of the power of imagination over sense, seeing that arsenic owes its favour with the secret poisoner in great measure to its being nearly tasteless!

Mental representation so intense as to become mental presentation is a faculty of mind apt especially to be met with among certain artists. It was very remarkable in that strange and eccentric genius, William Blake; he used habitually to see his conceptions as actual images or visions. " You have only to work up imagination to the state of vision and the thing is done," was his account of the process.

If hallucinations are engendered now in the way just described we may be sure that it was so in times past, when their real nature, so far from being known in the least, was not even suspected. It was natural then, nay, inevitable, to think them spiritual or supernatural apparitions. What other interpretation could be given of them? In the nature of things, too, they could not fail to occur more easily to savage and barbarous minds, less amply stored with faculties,

* M. Taine (*De l'Intelligence*) is the authority for this statement.

and these loosely federate, just as they occur more readily in young children than in adults; and, occurring, they would be more sure to compel belief, seeing that there was no store of natural knowledge to sit in judgment upon them, much less to give a natural explanation of them. The brain-centres being more complex and more finely and firmly knit in civilized persons, consolidate with the stable organization of more numerous and true relations with external nature, there is less facility for a part to let itself go out of relations with other parts into illusive activity and its accompanying vividness of presentation. Moreover, another and allied result of the more complex and compact mental fabric is the strong, silent inhibition of childish imaginations of the natural and the supernatural; wild flights of the puerile kind are impossible from the solid basis of assimilated facts and relations, imagination is imbued with the sober spirit of a large capitalized experience.

No more nowadays does the awed rustic hurry past the churchyard at night with palpitating heart, for the ghost is not seen there as once it was, because it is not believed in as once it was. The idea, if it arise, is faint and formless—too weak to attain by intensification the vivid energy to become an image, either of itself or with the help of a friendly moonbeam; it lacks the adequate basis of emotional belief. Instantly and unconsciously controlled by a silent process of inhibition, owing to the positive knowledge incorporate in the structure of a well-balanced and fairly cultured brain, it stirs no emotional agitation there; for the accumulations of natural knowledge which constitute the mental fabric of the modern disbelief in ghosts signify definitely organized cerebral tracks that exert a silent, steady inhibition effectively to prevent or restrain the uprising idea.

As the belief in ghosts and other spiritual apparitions has prevailed among peoples in all times and places, and still lingers among savages, it must have its deep foundations either in the facts of nature or in the constitution of human nature. The scientific enquirer is bound either to account for the apparitions as coinages of brain such as " ecstasy is very cunning in," or to frankly acknowledge them to be indubitable instances of spiritual beings taking human or other shapes (for dogs and other animals have frequently thus appeared) and becoming visible to men. The little room which they have now in human thought in comparison with the large space which they once filled, and the rareness and fineness of them now in comparison with their frequency and crudeness in the past, show that the tendency of modern enquiry and thought is to thin and subtilize them into extinction.

In this connection it is right to note that the visions seen in different times and places have been in keeping with the ideas or beliefs of the age and people. The apparitions of barbarous differ from those of savage peoples, and those of cultured from those of barbarous peoples : they change in character with the changing phases of intellectual development. Visions of Satan were common in the Middle Ages, but they seldom or never occur now. Luther's notions of the devil's personality and doings were very much on a par with those of a Saxon peasant of his time, he having no doubt whatever that witches frequently had carnal intercourse with their familiar devils ; * he was not surprised, therefore, to see the devil come into his cell and proceed to make a great noise behind the stove, or to hear him walking in the cloister above his cell at night. But is there an instance on record of ancient Greek or Roman seeing

---

* So also Sir Thomas Browne. " For my part I have ever believed and do now know that there are witches. They that doubt of these do not only deny them, but spirits ; and are obliquely, and upon consequence, a sort not of infidels, but Atheists. . . . I could believe that spirits use with men the act of carnality ; and that in both sexes. I conceive they may assume, steal, or contrive a body wherein there may be action enough to content decrepit lust or passion to satisfy more active veneries."—*Rel. Med.*

the devil? Or did ever ancient Greek or Roman, by private bargain, sell his soul to him for earthly pleasure and prosperity, as so many persons suffered death for doing in the Middle Ages? The Satan whom Luther rudely assaulted by flinging an inkstand at his head had not then been invented; the notion of him not existing, hallucination did not take his shape.

When Christianity spread among the heathen their dethroned pagan gods were banished to lonely places and dreary caverns in the forests and on the hills, stigmatized as evil spirits, and declared to be the workers of the calamities, sicknesses, and other ills which men suffered; for the new gods of the triumphant faith degraded the vanquished gods of the old faith into devils, as the conquering nations made slaves of the conquered. It is hard to say whether Satan exists still, a last survival of these dethroned gods, so vague, inconsistent, and obscure is the language used by those who talk and write about him; but, if he survive, it is certainly as the dim image of his old self, having the shadow only of his former power and state.

What would a Roman cardinal, could he dare to think sincerely and to speak sincerely what he thinks, say now of the Bull of Innocent VIII sanctioning and stimulating the torture and burning of witches? Or a Protestant archbishop think of Luther's opinion that the devil was the cause of devastating storms and other calamities; that blind, lame, dumb persons and idiots were persons in whom devils had established themselves; that physicians who tried to cure their infirmities as if they proceeded from natural causes were ignorant blockheads who knew nothing of the power of the devil? Barbarous nations everywhere still hold much the same opinions; knowing that they suffer injury and death at the hands of their fellows, they conclude that sickness and death are caused by the secret sorcery or other evil doing of one of their kind who works invisibly.

So much for the two principal modes of origin of hallucinations—that is to say, either primarily in the senses or their sensory and associated motor tracts, or primarily in the higher centres of thought. The division is a necessary one, because the distinction is evident between hallucinations that are in manifest relation with the thoughts, therefore of more specially mental origin and nurture, and hallucinations that are not in manifest relation with the thoughts, being of sensory and, so to speak, more bodily origin and nurture. However, notwithstanding the needful distinction, it is certain that the origin of hallucinations is most often mixed, and their nature always so when their true character is not appreciated by the subject; sense and thought combining to produce the effect and it being impossible to say which is first and most at fault. Nor could it well be otherwise, seeing how intimate and essential is the connection between the respective nerve-centres of thought and sense, whereby they act together in co-ordination and unity of function.

One consideration more in this connection : that in most cases in which an idea of the thought-centres becomes hallucination compelling belief, and in most cases in which hallucination originating in sense overrules reason, there is discoverable, when adequate enquiry is made (I exclude the case of gross cerebral disease), a natural or acquired infirmity of nervous constitution, a flaw or frailty tending to what it ends in.

There is this more to be said of the hallucination which is in vital relation with the thought—namely, that, although the hallucination is a phantom, the thought may none the less be valid, the hallucination being a sort of incidental dross thrown off by its glowing heat. When it is gravely considered how great a part hallucinations have played at critical periods of human history, being regarded as divine visions and infusing the conviction of supernatural countenance and help in the work done, the cynic might triumph, and the believer in the hopes of his kind despair, were it necessary to believe that human progress ever rested entirely on so rotten a basis. But if a person has been fired by a fervent faith and, so inspired, has done epoch-making work in the world, what matters it that he had a helpful hallucination? The primary and real force in the work was not the hallucination, that was adjunct only, it was the antecedent or concomitant heat of feeling and faith; and the work done, whether good or bad, was none the less real because it had not the particular supernatural sign or seal claimed for it. Had Mahomet never seen the angel Gabriel it is probable that the great mission of overthrowing idolatry and polytheism, and of welding scattered tribes into a powerful nation, would have been accomplished by him or by some other prophet who, formulating in thought the brooding *nisus* of the time and fusing energies into compact unity of aim by glowing feeling, would have risen up to do what the world had then at heart.

How inestimable, then, the service sometimes rendered to mankind by the few who can think and, thinking, do differently from the herd! A well-balanced brain, adjusted fitly by every facet of it to every aspect of its surroundings, so far as these are known, is plainly not an engine to break up the medium and to make new surroundings, evolutional or revolutional; the required brain for that purpose is one which, not being in stable repose of faculties and circumstances, but unstable, with a preponderating tension in one direction, is instigated by an unrest, divine or demonic, urging it to discharge itself in the disruption of the old medium. It is the fit instrument provided by nature, where its productive energies are not effete, to prevent stagnation, and not provided when they are effete.

The real difficulty in putting forth a new principle is to disregard meditative doubts and paralysing fears, to dare the revolt in the beginning; for if the principle has vitality it initiates a stream of change which

draws to itself a succession of reinforcing affluents
and flows with steadily gathering force. It is to make
the initial start that a mind emancipated though it
be by natural defects of constitution from the customary inhibitions of thought and feeling has its
special and excellent uses.

The foregoing considerations respecting the origin
and nature of visions and hallucinations make it plain
that phenomena really morbid have uniformly been
mistaken for supernatural appearances all the world
over : so much lies beyond dispute. Furthermore,
it is indisputable that temperaments prone naturally
to lapse into morbid action have been purposely
selected, and means suited to induce morbid action
of them systematically used, in order to obtain the
visions. But to leap forthwith from that conclusion
to the unqualified assertion that all visions of the
supernatural everywhere have had a like pathological
origin and no higher origin, is to make a generalization
which many will vehemently repudiate. Every creed
is prompt to protest that there are essential differences between the hallucinations of mental disorder
and the authentic visions of its inspired seership.
Who, then, will expound the differential characters ?

The followers of a particular religion cannot do
otherwise than repudiate the divine authority of the
supernatural events of other religions, rejecting rival
visions, not because of any evidence of genuineness
or falsity discoverable in the features of the visions
themselves, but because every creed must begin by
tacitly begging the whole question in its favour. For
to start with the implicit postulate that its revelation
is the true one is to guarantee beforehand the truth
of the supernatural visions which occur under its
auspices. Thus the vision's truth rests entirely upon
the truth of the revelation, albeit the fact does not
hinder the vision from being quoted in turn as proof
of the revelation; the proving and the proved going
to work reciprocally to hold one another up. The
vital question really is whether any vision bears a

supernatural superscription on its face, and, if so, what the superscription is and who is the infallible to read its infallible testimony.

Those who have investigated the nature and varieties of morbid hallucinations on the one hand, and on the other hand have closely studied the elaborate descriptions of their supernatural experiences by canonized saints who hold high places in the sacred calendar, have not been able to discover differential features. For example, taking hallucinations of hearing, which are most common hallucinations among the insane, and comparing them with the divine voices or *locutions*, which are the least suspicious of the supernatural experiences that so many saints of ecclesiastical history testify to having had, it clearly appears that there is not a single feature in the one which has not its counterpart in the other. No doubt the divine locutions were often intellectual only, the words, though duly formed, being heard internally, as it were, as if they were somehow inspired into the understanding, not spoken actually to the ears; but that is not a mark of distinction, since it is equally true of many morbid hallucinations. The insane person does not always hear the voices as distinct articulate utterances from without; he is careful sometimes, when questioned about them, to explain that they are in his head—interior voices, thoughts which he hears within, rather than words actually heard with his ears from without.

It is difficult for the individual not to think of voices of the kind as in some sort supernatural, when he feels the ideas which they suggest or express to be contrary to the tenor of his true thoughts and feeling; to be forced into his mind against his will and by no known law of association; to play their repugnant parts there without consciousness on his part of the smallest co-operation in their doings; and yet to appeal to him more distinctly and to possess him more intimately than ideas which he is conscious of having formed himself. Practically, he feels himself to be a divided, as he is a distracted, self; one part of him being possessed by a mysterious power which subtracts it from his real self, dominates it, and thrusts its promptings into the mental operations with the perversity and persistence of a malignant demon in possession of him : perhaps it is the devil himself whom he accuses of working on his spirit to suggest wicked thoughts and feelings. What matters it that all the world differs from him, and that everybody he meets, learned or unlearned, is ready to assure him that no external agency can possibly do that which he thinks is done to him, when the subjective reality of the experience is so vivid, so mysterious, so overpowering? Under the paralysing intensity of its coercive sway the very impossibility of a natural explanation becomes a reason for impotent belief in that which subverts all the principles of the rational understanding.

If one refers to the experience of St. Theresa, who justly holds the foremost place as an authority concerning the nature of divine locutions, it appears that, although she lays down rules by which to distinguish between them and mere ideas of the understanding, not one of the rules serves to distinguish them from hallucinations. It is no mark of distinction that in divine locutions, as she says, the words are very distinctly formed, but not heard by the bodily ear; that they are much more clearly understood than they would be if so heard. Nor is it a mark of distinction that there is no escape from them; that it is not in the person's power to turn away his attention from them, as it is with locutions of his own mind; that he must listen whether he desires it or not. That they come with singular authority when not desired and when the understanding is occupied with other things, and that they may not come when desired, whereas the locutions of the understanding come whenever we like—these, again, are not extraordinary characters, but characters which they have in common with ordinary hallucinations.

If there be no objective mark in the supernatural communication itself to distinguish it from hallucination, it is certainly not possible to accept the individual's intimate certitude as guarantee of its divine nature. To do that would be to admit the authenticity of every supernatural experience of the kind which any one in any country has ever believed himself to have; nor would it be possible to stop there, seeing that every madman labouring under morbid hallucination might claim a similar authority for his intense assurance. The latter we know to be deceived; the former we may justly suppose equally likely to be deceived, and far more likely, because more tempted by subtle interests, to deceive. To place any faith in testimony liable to two such powerful causes of fallacy, when it conflicted with the unfailing experience of all men of good sense with regard to a regular order of nature, would be a subversion of the principles of reasoning on which knowledge is based. Not one of the contending religions exacts interruptions of the regular course of nature on behalf of other religions or of mankind generally; the demand is only for its private behoof. "This is the true revelation because it is mine" is an idolatry of the *teste meipso* which, however satisfactory to self, cannot be expected to satisfy other selves.

The objection that a direct communication from the Deity would be a violation of the laws of nature is not answered by the old and stale argument that the divine locution might take place in conformity with a higher law than the known laws of nature, being a temporary discontinuity, not a violation of them—a special supersession only of their function for the occasion. To a being who lives in nature, and must live by knowledge of it, the supernatural has no pertinence since it is not natural. The occurrence of a supernatural event in direct opposition to its known natural order would be nothing else but the temporary abolition of the known properties and relations of things and the utter confounding of human experience—of that same experience which alone is our authority for believing human testimony; not the mere interruption or suspension of known law, but the negation of all law based upon the uniformity of experience within its range. The very basis of natural knowledge would be destroyed; no belief could ever have the certitude that it was in conformity with experience, no generalization ever be trusted, nor could an instant's confidence be felt as to what would come to pass from hour to hour; it would be no matter thenceforth how many miracles, big or little, happened, nor how often nor how seldom they happened: the universe would practically be a chaos, not a cosmos. If the law of gravitation may be suspended even for a second of time without the universe going to wreck, then it is clear that there is no law of gravitation at all; for the suspension of a second would serve as well as the suspension of a century.

Were the arguments in support of supernatural communications worth anything the communications themselves could not fail seriously to weaken them; so uncertain, confused, contradictory, and sometimes ridiculous are they. Moreover, they are invariably rejected by those who, not believing, need to be convinced, and invariably accepted by those who, believing, have no need to be convinced. Comparing, then, as Hume recommends, the instances of the violation of truth in the testimony of men with the instances of the violation of the laws of nature by supernatural visions and voices in order to judge which of them is least extraordinary and most likely to happen, the veracity of the testimony in such case would be perhaps a more miraculous event than the event which it was adduced to establish.

CHAPTER IV

MANIA AND DELUSION

HAVING said so much concerning hallucination, its interpretation and its misinterpretations, there is no need to say much concerning the features of more positive mental disorder. If a person has an insane hallucination and, believing it not insane, suffers it to rule his thoughts and conduct, it is evident that his reason shares in the disorder; for if reason were not overruled and deluded it might be expected to reason against it, if not to reason it away, and in any event to keep it sequestered in harmless isolation, as a sort of mental alien, instead of receiving it into its intimacy, naturalizing it there, and admitting it to full rights of mental citizenship.

It is not easy to conceive now that the incoherent ravings of madness were once thought to be the utterances of a god in possession of the man; yet so it was in olden times.* In the Hebrew and Greek languages the same words were used to denote the ravings of insanity and the often equally unintelligible ravings of the diviner or revealer of divine things; so that it became necessary, in the course of time, to distinguish the mania which was disease from the mania which was inspiration proceeding from the gods or God. In both cases the individual was transported by a mysterious power into an extraordinary mental state in which he became the organ of strange utterances; only it was perceived soon in some cases that the state must be madness, whether devil-inflicted or not, because the thoughts, feelings, words, and conduct of the individual were thoroughly insensate

* Οὐδεὶς ἔννους μαντεύεται, said Philo; *i.e.*, No one prophesies in his right mind.

and destructive of social order; while in the other
cases, where the oracle was delivered in a more sober
and coherent fashion, the notion of supernatural
infusion preserved its credit for a long time, lost it
slowly, has not yet lost it entirely.

It was no valid objection to the ravings of the
inspired person that to all outward seeming they were
as unintelligible nonsense as the ravings of madness.
That was their sacred seal and privilege, for the prophet or interpreter was the necessary complement of
the oracle; his special function it was to find and
expound the sense of the incoherent nonsense which
the God-struck person—the theoleptic—poured out
under divine compulsion: he was one who, like
Daniel, " had understanding in all visions and
dreams " and to whom they revealed their dark and
sometimes awful meaning, as the mysterious writing
on the wall revealed Belshazzar's doom to Daniel.
To the one was given " divers kinds of tongues, and
to another the interpretation of tongues "; " for he
that speaketh in a tongue speaketh not unto men,
but unto God; for no man understandeth." Greater,
then, according to St. Paul, was he that prophesied
(that is, expounded the dark sayings) than he who
spake in tongues, since the Church received no edify-
ing from the latter, except he were interpreted.*
Moreover, the confusion was sure to be so great, if
many were assembled and all spake with tongues, that
unbelievers would certainly believe appearances and
say they were mad. Therefore it was meet that not
more than two, or at most three, should speak in
tongues—and that not together, but in turn—and
that one should interpret. In the delirious utterance
itself there was nothing whatever by which ordinary
people could distinguish it from actual delirium, which

---

* The meaning of the word " prophet " was not then,
as now, one who predicted events to come, but one who
interpreted and expounded mysterious ravings, dark oracles,
unknown tongues, and the like unintelligible utterances of
the God-possessed person.

it exactly resembled; the privileged interpreter was required to reveal its occult and holy meaning. Meanwhile the central difficulty was only moved, not removed; for no provision was made to guarantee the veracity, competence, and infallibility of the interpreter.

Such was the state of belief at one time. But there was another reason besides a superstitious belief in the divine inspiration of raving nonsense for the opinion that prophets were transported out of themselves by supernatural influx to say what they could not have said out of their own natural resources : that was the impressive spectacle of the extraordinary spontaneity and brilliant flow of ideas exhibited by a mind in the inflamed state of activity which is often prelusive of actual delirium or mania ; for there is then a singular upsurging into consciousness of the latent possessions of experience, so that the elated person, enchanted with the revelation of unsuspected wealth of thought and feeling, exults in a rapid rush of ideas, a vividness of memory, a freshness of feeling, a fertility of associations and combinations of ideas, and a facility of expression that seem to him almost miraculous.

A good illustration of this inflamed state of mind, happily called by him a state of mental ignition, has been furnished by Ruskin's description of his experience of a mental illness to which he succumbed in consequence of overwork, as his physicians thought. He, however, was able, he believed, to appreciate the state of things much better than they did and to distinguish what was definitely diseased in the brain-action from what was simply curative—had there been time enough—of the wounded nature in him.

" Namely, first, the precise and sharp distinction between the state of morbid inflammation of brain which gave rise to false visions, and the not morbid, however dangerous, states of more or less excited temper, and too much quickened thought, which gradually led up to the illness, accelerating in action during the eight or ten days preceding the actual giving-way of the brain; and yet, up to the transitional moment of the first hallucination, entirely healthy, and, in the full sense of the word, 'sane'; just as the natural inflammation about a healing wound in flesh is sane up to the transitional edge where its mass passes at a crisis into morbific, or even mortified, substance.'

This more or less inflamed, yet still perfectly healthy, condition of mind, as he miscalls it, he found to be " a great additional force, enabling me to discern more clearly, and say more vividly, what for long years it had been in my heart to say." Such the ineffable joy of delivery! Then he goes on to try to show that his writings and sayings and doings during this state had more method and consistency in their seeming incoherence than people thought, and were not so wanting in truth and soberness as they looked on the face of them; albeit admitting that some things had been said imprudently, and even incontinently, because he could not at the moment hold his tongue about what vexed or interested him, or returned soothingly to his memory.

The distinction between the two states of premaniacal brilliancy and of positive maniacal disorder is not unknown to physicians, as Ruskin might easily have discovered had he been at the pains to refer to any medical treatise giving a description of the premonitory symptoms of an attack of mania; but the significance of the mental ignition of the first stage, so well described by him, is not interpreted by them as he interpreted it in his case. The state is neither sane nor salutary, no more than inflammation is as sane or salutary as he ignorantly supposed. Always the best healing of a wound takes place without inflammation—by what Hunter called " first intention "; and the great aim of surgical treatment, and its eminent success at the present day, is, by excluding causes of irritation, to get healing without inflammation, or, if that cannot be done entirely, with the least inflammation possible; for the inflammation is not helpful and welcome, but hurtful and unwelcome, to quick and sound healing, being the exponent and effect of damaged structure and incontinent function—of lowered life; a stage of the descent towards, and a less degree of, that which Ruskin calls " morbific, or even mortified, substance," and only welcome as falling short of the worst stage.

So likewise it is with the premonitory state of mental ignition : he whose mind is thus on fire, happy though he be in the glowing consciousness of extraordinarily clear insight, of brilliant flashes of thought, of exalted powers of expression, is nowise so sane and sensible as he imagines; one thing he lacks pretty completely—namely, sound appreciation and solid judgment ; and one thing he cannot do—namely, hold himself in and hold his tongue. He cannot truly apprehend other things and selves in just relations to himself and in their just proportions; full of self and incontinent of thought, feeling, and speech, he runs over in the exuberant expression of it, his keen self-love reacting in such high delirious strain against its previous humiliations, real or imagined; and the estimate which he forms of the value of what he then thinks and says, vividly exaggerated as it is by the intensity of personal feeling and the suspension of the proper qualifying inhibitions, is something of the same kind as that of the dreamer who is delighted with his power to compose brilliant poetry or prose, which he perhaps discovers, if a line or two remain in his memory on waking, to be not even brilliant nonsense. The prudent aim of a wise physician who was summoned to advise in such case, mindful that fever of mind is no more healthy than fever of body, would be to abate the mental ignition by enjoining rest and quiet of mind in order to get sane and sober thought, just as his aim would be to subdue inflammation in order to get the wound healed.

A feature in Ruskin's case, as described by himself, has its special instruction—namely, his deep reluctance to acknowledge sincerely the madness of what he thought and did, and his desire to make out his conduct to have been more consistent and reasonable than it looked to others. Now, this is a circumstance not uncommon after mental illness—very notable after some forms thereof—especially after that intrinsic derangement which grows stealthily as a pathological development of character and is much a growth of self-love or egoism, as distinguished from the extrinsic insanity, so to speak, which, not native to the character, befalls the person accidentally as a foreign invader. The persistence of a positive morbid hallucination or delusion after all the other delirious symptoms of the malady have gone, which is noticed in some cases of otherwise apparently pretty complete mental recovery, is a more striking example of the same tendency. Such are the natural infirmities of human nature that it is hard for wounded self-love to accept sincerely the humiliation of its entire overthrow; it strains instinctively to find redeeming excuses and explanations, or takes obstinate refuge in some entrenchment of the ruins from which it refuses to be dislodged by evidence and argument.

There are two types of insane delusions, of quite contrary nature, characterizing the two leading classes of mental disorder, and corresponding to the two ordinary moods of depression and exaltation to which every mind is liable. In the one case, the afflicted person is in a state of abject fear and misery, full of vague apprehensions of evil to come, incapable of heart in his affairs or of hope of them, apathetic, inert, despairing, and sure that he is, or is about to be, overwhelmed by some unspeakable calamity— perhaps it is that he is forsaken by God and given over to eternal damnation : this is, so to speak, the delirious climax of a natural mood of melancholy. In the other case, we are confronted with one who, excessively elated and self-confident, is buoyant and busy, making light of difficulties, despising apprehensions, eager to plan and bold to execute the projects which he is prolific in forming, and who, perhaps, growing in presumption as his mind grows more and more inflamed, in the end rises to the conviction that he is one of the great personages of the world : this is, so to speak, the delirious climax of a natural mood of elated feeling and sanguine thought.

It is interesting to notice how these two contrary dispositions have given rise to two contrary forms of religious superstition. The gloomy and apprehensive mind, dreading all sorts of unknown evils from unknown agents, has had recourse to propitiations, ceremonies, sacrifices, and prayers, in order to placate the invisible powers whom it feared; has implored and purchased the mediating help of those who pretended to direct converse and influence with them, and the interest of whose craft it was to magnify its terrors; and in its terrified credulity has been the easy victim of designing knavery. Here is a common and abiding, as it was probably an original, source of vulgar superstition. The sanguine and confident mind, on the other hand, indulging high notions suited to its exalted mood and aspirations, and giving free flight to its imagination, grows to a great height of presumption, and finally, when stirred to the requisite glow of excitement, to transports and ecstasies which, being accompanied with a delirium of delight and quite beyond the reach of ordinary faculties, are attributed to the immediate inspiration of the Deity, of whom the favoured individual thenceforth regards himself as the chosen oracle.* Such is the natural origin and growth of the enthusiastic fanatic who claims the authority of a direct divine inspiration, and, taking the lead in thought and action, commonly dominates and leads the anxious and self-distrusting temperament.

Considering impartially the case of Mahomet, it repugns reason that throughout his career he was only the clever impostor who duped others without duping himself. Small indeed was his encouragement to begin the dangerous and difficult enterprise

* Hume's Essay *Of Superstition and Enthusiasm.*

of his life, and almost unexampled the steadfast constancy of conviction and devotion needed to carry it through; for he had to face the anger and alienation of his friends and relatives, to give up an honourable place in his tribe, to hide as an outcast in caverns in order to save his life.

Mahomet was forty years old when the truth was first revealed to him, and in three years he had gained thirteen followers! Now, as it is certain that any one is immensely comforted and fortified in his conviction the moment another person shares it, seeing that he may then reasonably hope it is not mere madness—Mahomet's faith, when prone to falter and despair before universal disbelief, being sustained by the single supporting faith of his old wife, Kadijah— it is hard to believe that pure imposture had strength enough to bear triumphantly the stress which he endured. His was a venture which it was not likely to repay the ambition of imposture to begin, hardly within the forces of fraud to carry through.

But a vindication of Mahomet's sincerity must needs be at the expense of his sanity; for the allegations that he ascended into heaven, as he said he did, that he was visited by angels, and that he wrote down the Koran exactly as it was dictated to him supernaturally, are fables fit only for a mental nursery.

Having a new and great work to accomplish in the world, a new start of nature's development in its human domain, since he was entrusted with the message which nature yearned to be delivered of at that time and in that place; urged consequently by an impelling inspiration whose mysterious thrill might well seem supernatural; his imagination, working under its supreme strain, would lay hold of every help, genuine or fictitious, offered by the incidents of its glowing energy. He knew not himself how much he was impostor and how much saint—what prophet ever did?—nature so mixing the proportions of good and bad in the composition of the prophet as to leave it uncertain how far his work is due to the worst or best element in him.

A signal instance of one who posed and was adored by disciples as an inspired prophet of God is Emanuel Swedenborg, the founder of the Church of the New Jerusalem. The son of a somewhat mystical mother and a singularly self-complacent and self-sufficient father—a Swedish bishop, who always managed to persuade himself that his own worldly interests were entirely other-worldly and identical with the will of God, and who was sure he had cured disease miraculously by his prayers—Swedenborg inherited in his nature a serene and boundless self-sufficiency along with a strong mystical tendency.

It was in an extraordinary vision which he had when he was fifty-six years old that the being who appeared to him said, " I am God, the Lord, the Creator and Redeemer of the world. I have chosen thee to unfold the spiritual sense of the Holy Scriptures. I will Myself dictate to thee what thou shalt write." The visitation was the forerunner of an attack of acute mania—so overwhelming the pressure of supernatural influx upon the mental equilibrium of the natural man—which lasted for a few weeks ; on recovery from which he was what he remained for the rest of his life—either, as his disciples think, a holy seer endowed with the faculty of conversing with spirits and angels in heaven and hell, and in whom the Lord Jesus Christ made His second coming for the institution of a new Church, described in the Revelation under the figure of the New Jerusalem ; or, as those who are not disciples think, an interesting and harmless monomaniac, who, among many foolish sayings, said many wise and good things attesting the wreck of a mind of large original endowment, intellectual and moral. Such the momentous difference of opinion possible, in an age esteeming itself the most enlightened age of the world, between two human beings of equal capacity and understanding, each as eager as the other to know the truth and believe it !

CHAPTER V

NATURAL AND SUPERNATURAL RELIGION

THE common principle of the religions and morality of all ages and places has been that of self-renunciation —self-suppression, obligatory or voluntary, for the good of the family and the community in the first instance, and the rise and expansion of this discipline of self afterwards, in ascending moral growth, to self-denial, self-sacrifice, self-renunciation. Rudimentary or complete, it is that which is their common inspiring principle; that in them which, by a survival of the fittest, has continued to be; that which is the cement of social life where theology is wanting; that, therefore, which is the destined note of the ultimate system. The sublime truths and lofty principles of morality were in nowise Christian discoveries; they are to be found plainly enunciated in religions prior to Christianity and in the writings of heathen philosophers; what it did was to supply the powerful arguments of Heaven and Hell to enforce the practice of the precepts.

Very different has it been with the theological systems of the different religious creeds that have risen and set in the revolution of things. There has been no agreement between the many and various nations concerning the shapes and doings of the supernatural; nor was agreement possible, seeing that there was no common method of enquiry and reasoning by which men might reach a common conclusion, nor any common standard by which to measure the value of the different conclusions actually reached. Being of supernatural origin and authority in each case, the revelation was the special gift or privilege of the particular people to whom it was made—part of their mode of thought and feeling, which, like language, differentiated them—the bond and symbol of national unity. It is notorious that we meet with no more complete dividing barrier between Christian and Moslem at the present day than their different religions, while the different sects of the Christian religion, much as they profess to have in common beneath differences, and little as their differences signify, are separated by acrid animosities which plainly prove how much more human than Christian nature there is in pious persons.

In essential meaning religion is the universal bond or cement of society; religions therefore are many, and that religion is the best which inspires and holds together the best social system in the most complete harmony of parts, inspiring the units of it so to do those things which ought to be done and to leave undone those things which ought not to be done towards one another, as to keep it in the best health —that is to say, most holy.

So far from sound religion requiring mortification of mind and body by gloom, sadness, remorse, fastings, penances, and other austerities of the kind, in order to propitiate and please a dread supernatural being, it calls for the full and joyous development of all the functions, bodily and mental, of the individual, in order to perfect the natural being. If true holiness is true healthiness, that is the best religion which fits the individual best for all his relations as a social being. Nothing can be greater folly than to separate the human and the animal in the man, and to set them over against one another as different and hostile factors having different ends. The human could no more exist without the animal than a plant could live without its root; and the wise person who would make the best of himself and the most of life will take good care of his body, gratifying every sense as well and in as many ways as he can, so long as it is done

E (N. C.)

with due regard to the rights of other senses and the well-being of the whole organism.*

The exaggerated and unwholesome egoism which takes not the inward way of solitary mysticism, of asceticism, of sentimental brooding, but the outward way of fanatical propagation of new doctrine along with passionate assault on old doctrine, seems on the whole to be less demoralizing to the individual, and may be more useful to the community, if the new thing chance to be a true development. But, when such is its fortune, are we to suppose, because of its truth, that it owed its inspiration and power to more than natural sources? Is it a supernatural event to be helplessly wondered at? Or is it a natural event to be studied diligently according to the positive methods of science? In times past, when there was almost entire ignorance of natural causes, the invention of supernatural agencies was legitimate and necessary; when kings governed by divine right prophets could not well claim less than divine inspiration; but in what light ought such inventions and pretensions to be viewed by an age which is occupied systematically in searching out the natural causes and laws of events, and in dissipating the mysteries of supernatural phenomena?

If the part played by supernatural visions and miracles in the propagation of a faith was subsidiary to the doctrine which alone guaranteed them, it follows that they may really be dropped out of account without injury to the essentials of the faith which they encumber and sometimes embarrass with their help; not otherwise, in fact, than as those signs and wonders that occurred in connection with abortive religious movements have fallen into oblivion or been discarded as illusions. Not so easily, certainly,

---

* Under the conditions of being able to renounce any or every indulgence if there be good reason for the self-denial. That is true and healthy *asceticism*; it is the element of truth too, perhaps, which underlies the squalid travesties of the half-insane and histrionic ascetic.

forasmuch as they obtain a reflected credit from the successful work of which they are the fringing incidents. Being so closely linked to the movement of human development through the ages, the reluctance is great to part with them; faith clings to the hallucinations as if to relinquish them would be to repudiate the movement; its genuineness makes up for their unreality and infuses the minds of believers with the bias necessary to subjugate reason and to compel belief in them. Nevertheless, it clearly appears that morbid hallucinations and supernatural visions are upon the same level in respect of inherent authority, which is actually *nil*; the credit or discredit which they have being in both cases derivative.

PART III

THEOPNEUSTICISM: THE ATTAINMENT OF SUPERNATURAL KNOWLEDGE BY DIVINE INSPIRATION

SECTION I

ECSTATIC INTUITION

THE various means by which, in different ages and places, the supernatural has been diversely revealed to different people may be grouped roughly into three principal classes: first, the visible appearance of the god, or of his messenger or angel, who revealed directly to the favoured person, by visible signs or articulate voice, that which he was chosen to know, each people having its own god or gods, whose revelations exactly answered to the measure of its intellectual and moral growth; secondly, a mysterious and overpowering possession, by the god, of the individual, who, thrown thereby into violent agitation of body and mind, or into trance-like unconsciousness of surrounding things, poured forth unconsciously, or in obedience to irresistible impulse, utterances that were sometimes quite incoherent and unintelligible, requiring a special interpreter or prophet to make known the meaning of them, sometimes sufficiently coherent to take their place, when written down, as holy scriptures; thirdly, the exaltation of the individual into a spiritual ecstasy, during which, rapt from things of sense and transported out of himself into direct communion with God, he discerns transcendent truths of the spiritual world quite beyond his natural apprehension by sense and reason.

It is the third method, that of spiritual impregnation, which alone has vitality now among educated persons in civilized countries.

What, then, is the real nature of this ecstatic intuition? Is it a clear and sure means of acquiring truths of the spiritual world, a genuine divine illumination, and the means by which alone it is vouchsafed to man to learn them? At the outset note has to be taken of the fact that it is a state which is not peculiar to any one people, or to the disciples of any one religion. Brahmins and Mahometans, as well as Buddhists and Christians, the devout votaries of all sorts and conditions of religion, have discovered and used the methods of inducing the abnormal state of the nervous system; all alike have perceived the necessity of performing the kind of mental dislocation which is called the abstraction of the mind from the body, in order to enter into direct communion with God.

The mode of the operation is in this wise : by intense and prolonged concentration of thought into one channel, the concentration being aided by fixing the gaze intently for some time on a particular spot —whether it be an external object such as a crucifix, or a particular part of the body such as the pit of the stomach—the fitly disposed mind is thrown eventually into a cramp-like ecstasy in which sense and reason are suspended, conscious individuality lost in a transport which is felt as an absorption into the divine being, and ineffable truths then revealed to the merged and enraptured soul, not by slow steps of discursive reason but by immediate and instant intuition.*

It results naturally from the employment of the method of ecstatic intuition by the votaries of

* Usually the Brahmin devotee keeps on murmuring to himself or inaudibly pronouncing the mystical " Om," his mind concentrated the while on the deity, until at last even thinking is extinct, personal individuality lost, and the soul merged into the universal soul.

different religions that the revelations are as diverse as the religions. The reason-transcending truths obtained in that way are Christian truths when Christians perform, they are quite different truths when a holy dervish or Brahmin works himself into a like transport. And the same thing is true of its use by two Christians of different habits of thought and feeling : St. Theresa's visions of God, for example, do not agree with the visions which Swedenborg had of Him, being indeed in some respects, especially in respect of the Trinity, quite contradictory; and the pious Unitarian's intuition of God lacks necessarily the Godhead of Christ. It is the pity of the method that, vitiated by the subjectivity of the individual, it necessarily fails to yield uniform results when used by the followers of different religions, by different followers of the same religion, even by the same person in differing moods and seasons of life.

Of this unique and mysterious method of obtaining revelations of the infinite by being at one time infinite and at another time finite, and of communicating in a finite capacity to finite beings experiences gained when infinite, it is necessary here to say only two things. First, the theory of it is evidently at bottom a refined evolution of the savage's cruder opinion that in dreaming the spirit leaves the body, coming back to it when the person awakes; not coming back to it at all when he dies, but flitting dismally in ghost-like disconsolateness about the scenes of its former joys and sorrows. Secondly, the method is uncertain and useless; uncertain, because the value of its results rests entirely upon the authority of the individual, who may be misled himself or may wilfully mislead; useless, because this possible vitiation renders it impossible ever to know when to depend upon it, seeing that there is no approved test by which to prove its differing results in the hands of different persons and to settle which is the true one.

SECTION II

ECSTASY OF FEELING

LARGE and comfortable use was made of the method of direct communion with God by the early Christians. They were the enthusiastic devotees of it, and in their practice it reached a delirious rapture and high repute, though never, perhaps, so ecstatic a detachment as among the Brahmins.

Saint Augustine has left on record in his *Confessions* an elaborate and instructive account of the long process of yearning thought and feeling through which he went in straining to attain to the ecstatic knowledge of God. Passing from the knowledge of things obtained through the bodily senses, whither to reach the faculties of beasts, and thence to the reasoning faculty, to which what is received from the senses is referred to be judged, as he said, and finding these all to be variable, his yearning and straining soul at last raised itself above its low understanding, withdrawing itself from things of sense and intellect, and reached by a sudden leap the knowledge of the unchangeable to be preferred to the changeable.

" And thus," he continues, " with the faith of one trembling glance it arrived at THAT WHICH IS. And then I saw the invisible things understood by the things which are made. But I could not fix my gaze thereon ; and, my infirmity being struck back, I was thrown again on my wonted habits, carrying along with me only a loving memory thereof, and a longing for what I had, as it were, perceived the odour of, but was not yet able to feed upon."

By concentration of his mental energies on a special tract of thought and feeling, and by a persistent keeping up of this train of activity, he was able after a time so to strain it that contact or circuit with other thoughts and feelings was broken, and freed for a time from their restraining hold—in fact, to dislocate it functionally; and the quasi-cataleptic or quasi-delirious condition thus engendered was accompanied by a transport of spiritual illumination and rapture. It was only, as he says, by passing beyond the power whereby he was united to the body and the powers of his nature, to the very soul of which God is the life, as it quickeneth and giveth life to the body, that he could ascend to Him. But the difficulty naturally was to perpetuate this extraordinary state. For although the result of its induction was that "Thou admittest me to an affection, very unusual, in my inmost soul, which, if it were perfected in me, I know not what in it would not belong to the life to come," yet, "through my miserable encumbrance, I sink down again into these lower things, and am swept back by custom and held back."

If the passing of St. Augustine's mind beyond the tie by which it was united to his body was the func- tional passing of a specially invoked and provoked cerebral tract out of its concord and relations with other tracts of the mental fabric and the suspension of their functions during the ultra-physiological exaltation of its exclusive activity, as I have given reasons to think, we need not wonder at, nor need he have accused, the encumbrances of flesh whereby he was unable to keep up the rapture, but was forced to fall back into the custom of lower things.

Ample and instructive evidence of the nature of the ecstatic transports, and of the actual visions some- times engendered in them, is furnished by the life of St. Theresa, as recorded by herself. A child of highly imaginative nature, which she eagerly nourished by clandestine reading of the romances of chivalry so popular in Spain in her day, she formed a deter- mined resolution, when eighteen years of age, after a mental struggle of three months' duration, "to bend her will to be a nun." In the convent to which she betook herself in pursuance of this aim her health gave way under the strain : she was subject to frequent fainting fits, so that she was obliged at last to be taken home by her friends ; the pain in her heart was just " as if it had been seized by sharp teeth," and " so great was the torment that it was feared that it might end in madness " ; she could not eat anything whatever, could only drink ; for four days she was insensible, and in such apparently hopeless state that a grave was prepared for her ; her tongue was bitten to pieces, and her body bent together like a coil of rope ; she could not stir arm, foot, hand, or head, could only move one finger of the right hand, and was moved by being carried from place to place in a sheet.* After three years of this miserable suffering a gradual restoration to health took place, owing to the prayers of St. Joseph (as she believed), a saint for whom she had an especial love and veneration. Such was the beginning of the religious career of that most distinguished lady who afterwards was the subject of those remarkable ecstatic visions which she has described with singular lucidity of thought and expression, and with such a display of practical sagacity as marked the daily work of her later life.

No ill effects followed the raptures when they were first experienced, but in the end they left her in pain over her whole body, as if her bones were out of joint ; the kind of pain which hysterical and epileptic persons suffer after their fits.†

These raptures of St. Theresa exercised much the minds of her confessors and spiritual advisers, who were puzzled and divided in opinion concerning their real nature. The positive conclusion come to on one occasion, after formal conferences of five or six

* Physicians at the present day who are familiar with this sort of illness describe it as hystero-epilepsy and treat it accordingly ; looking forward to a speedy cure of it when the patient can be taken away from her anxious and sympathetic friends—who, for the most part, increase it by their attentions and anxieties—and placed under suitable care and treatment.

† *Life of St. Theresa*, by the author of *Devotions Before and After Holy Communion*.

E 2

learned divines about her, was that she was deceived by Satan; and the judicious advice given to her in consequence was to communicate less frequently, to try to distract herself, and to be less alone. Even those who thought the raptures to be the work of the Spirit of God in her did not fail to discern a marked sensual flavour in some of them; one of the wisest and kindest of her confessors recommending her two things in consequence—namely, to resist to the utmost of her power the sensible sweetness and delight she felt in her rapture, and to practise greater outward mortification and penance.

Evidently the ardent spiritual love of the divine incarnate in human form did not always reach the perfect detachment and refinement of a pure spiritual communion with the divine not incarnate; it resulted sometimes in a voluptuous ecstasy or orgasm in which the saint felt herself received, like St. Catharine of Sienna, "as a veritable spouse into the bosom of her Saviour." Indeed, when treating of the mode of inducing these ecstasies by endeavouring "to imagine ourselves present with Christ and take delight in Him," Theresa combats particularly, in one chapter of her life, the opinion of those spiritual writers who think no bodily object should intervene in wholly spiritual contemplation; that we ought so to abstain from all bodily imagination in contemplation of the Divinity as to put away the consideration of Christ's humanity. This, she maintains, "is making the soul, as they say, to walk in the air; for it has nothing to rest on, how full soever of God it may think itself to be. . . . We are not angels—we have a body; to seek to make ourselves angels while we are on the earth, and so much on the earth as I was, is an act of folly." Sagacious Theresa! ever wiser than her guides; she saw clearly that, however intensely and perseveringly any one may spiritualize thought and feeling, he cannot, while in the flesh, immaterialize them entirely.

Later in life, when, being at the head of a convent,

she had to deal as lady-abbess with the troublesome ecstasies of hysterical nuns, it was plain to her that they were not always of a divine character; and she protested against confounding the true divine infla-tion—the state in which the understanding ceases to act because God suspends it—with those devotional states of self-enforced rapture in which suffocating feelings and invasions of sensuality betray delusion and the work of Satan. It is a distinction between love and lust which other authorities on like spiritual seizures were compelled, in face of the gross lubricity sometimes displayed in them, to make; just as it was necessary to discriminate between the mania which was the result of inspiration, a divine madness, and the mania which was madness. Then as now, how-ever, there was no criterion by which to distinguish the true from the false inspiration, the genuine from the counterfeit; the authorities of a particular creed, albeit in doubt sometimes whether the raptures of its votaries were divine, never doubting that the raptures of rival creeds were delusive and Satanic, and the subject of them being by the nature of the case unable to bring more proof in support of them than his private sense of personal certitude.

SECTION III

INTUITION OF THE HEART

WE mount at once into a fresher and more wholesome air when, leaving these regions of sublimated sensuality, we come to Pascal's account of the intuitive source of knowledge. That great thinker argues that we know truth, not by reason only, but by the heart; that it is by the heart that first principles, such as *space, time, motion, number*, are known; that it is on such intrinsic knowledge of the heart, as sure as that of reasoning, that reason must fundamentally base itself. Principles are felt, propositions are concluded; and it is as ridiculous for the reason to demand from the heart proof of its first principles in order to assent to them, as it would be ridiculous for the heart to demand from the reason a feeling of all the propositions which it demonstrates, in order to accept them. Thus it is with divine truths, which God alone can impart to the soul, and in the way that pleases Him best.

So far Pascal : whose doctrine is in the main adopted and followed by Cardinal Newman in his subtle and elaborate exposition of the grounds of human certitude.* For the distinction set forth at length by Newman between *real* and *notional* assents is the distinction drawn by Pascal between the immediate feeling of first principles and the derivative conclusions of reason. But it is incredible that Pascal could have endorsed the logic or accepted the results of Newman's deductions from first principles; for while he scouted the notion of direct communion with God, seeing no means of arriving at a knowledge of the incompre-

* *Grammar of Assent.*

130

hensible except through a mediator, Cardinal Newman managed to discover an image of God and a distinct apprehension of His attributes in the intuitions of conscience.

The way, he says, by which we gain an image of God and give a real assent to the proposition that He exists is by assuming as a first principle, as the foundation of all inquiry into the subject, that we have by nature a conscience—*i.e.*, a sense of right and wrong and a magisterial dictate to do the right. That granted, all else will follow from it; for it implies the recognition of a living object towards which it is directed. " Inanimate things cannot stir our affections; these are correlative with persons." If we feel responsibility this implies that there is one to whom we are responsible. And if the cause of this feeling does not belong to the visible world—a second implication, although Newman does not say so—the object to which it is directed must be supernatural and divine; and " thus the phenomena of conscience, as a dictate, avail to impress the imagination with the picture of a Supeme Governor, a Judge—just, powerful, all-seeing, retributive—and is the creative principle of religion, as the moral sense is the principle of ethics." * A signal triumph of intellectual conjuring to get such transcendent *doctrinal* consequences out of the simple *feeling* of conscience ! What in the end is it but to make God in Newman's own image—in the image, that is, of his moral judgment of things—to make his own mental idol ? And what is the certitude of the concluded *notional* product worth when it is the immediate *feeling* only which has certitude ? An idol is still an idol, though it be an idol of the heart.

However it be with particular differences between these two eminent authorities on the highest spiritual matters, they are at one in this general truth which is to be deemed indisputable—that the highest truths of

* *Grammar of Assent.*

Christian religion are to be known, and to be known only, by the heart; known as sensations are known, not by being apprehended but by being felt.

Is it true, then, and if true, how far true, that divine truths are apprehended by the heart and with intuitive certainty? Not the definite *doctrines* or *dogmas* of the Christian religion certainly; they are as distinct matters of intellectual apprehension as any other propositions in regard of which the understanding assents or dissents; to call them experiences of feeling, or to allege that they are known through feeling, would be to confound all distinction between understanding and feeling. Moreover, it would be to deny the capacity of elementary feeling of the things of highest human concern to all those people—the large majority of the human race—who cannot instinctively feel their truth and beauty. In order that the divine truths of Christianity may kindle a unison of feeling in the individual's heart his mind must, as Pascal and Newman carefully explain, be methodically moulded and attuned by fit training, not in the doctrines of the Scriptures only, but also in the canons and rites and offices of the Catholic Church, which is the repository of truth and the authorized and infallible interpreter of the ways of God to man: the reason must be resolutely, systematically, and perseveringly humiliated for the purpose of bringing it into a state in which, becoming foolish in order to be wise, it shall assent joyfully to truths that stultify it. High treason verily against reason had not reason been deposed. But it is a cardinal truth of theology that what is *nonsense* to reason may be *sense* in religion.

The differences among Christians respecting the essential tenets of their common creed, and the fierce persecutions with which the different sects in different times and places have rejoiced to pursue and afflict one another because of their irreconcilable differences of doctrinal opinion, are ample proof that doctrines are not matters of pure intuitive feeling. The prodigious importance ascribed to the minutest shades of doctrinal difference, " visible only to the nicest theological eye," is proof again how successfully man may so fashion himself artificially by special training as to sincerely think the veriest trivialities of thought to be transcendent things worth dying for and worth inflicting torture and death for. Nay, there need be no thought to wrangle about ; a name will do. A common Christianity has always been consistent with an uncommon hatred, and uncommonly cruel persecutions, of one another by differently thinking Christians.

In respect of the direct intuition of God which loving hearts achieve, matters are not left by those who practise it in nearly so secure a position of certitude as could be wished. For nowhere is more emphatic stress laid upon this method of communion, and more positive claim made for its absolute authority, than by spiritually minded Unitarians, who, having robbed the Triune Deity of that which Christians think an essential part of His Godhead, and thus fearfully mutilated and blasphemed Him in Christian eyes, exhaust the capacities of Christian emotion and language in endeavours to express the inexpressible sweetness of the beatific communion. With whom ? With God the Father, without God the Son ; not with the Christian's Father and Son in one God. It is a piously enthused Unitarian who enjoins upon us " to attain similitude and communion by loving self-abandonment " ; to think of God " coalescing with our highest nature, to subdue and mould it all into sympathy with His own perfectness " ; to " leave ourselves to the dear God who communes with us " ; to " look into the loving eyes themselves of all that is good and holy " ; and so on in like strains of emotional eloquence labouring to give effusive vent to ecstatic sentiments of the sweetness and joy of divine intoxication.* But to talk of " looking into the loving eyes " of " the dear God "—is that the decorous language of sober sense ? Is it not rather the incontinent over-

* Dr. Martineau, *Hours of Thought.*

flow of uninformed sentiment? Curious is it to see
how deeply men can intoxicate themselves with a fine
setting of melodious words which express no definite
ideas, but are pleasing discharges of vague and
incontinent emotion.

SECTION IV

THE PHYSICAL BASIS OF ECSTATIC INTUITION

How is any one, even the most highly favoured subject of a supernatural visitation, to be sure that it is objective reality, not subjective illusion? How can he safely say how much is verity, how much is vanity? He no doubt feels intensely sure; the beatific feeling is intrinsic proof to him; it supersedes and transcends all the processes of reason by which he ordinarily examines and certifies belief; infuses him with the thrill of an intuitive certainty. The strongest proofs of reason would add nothing to the overwhelming certitude; the strongest disproof of reason can take nothing from it. Nevertheless, it is possible he may be deceived; in his most ecstatic rapture he is still human, and it is human to err. That is the one certain thing in the uncertain business.

When close inquiry is made into the mental constitutions of those who are most sure of a faculty of spiritual intuition, and exult most to have and use it, good reasons of doubt present themselves. They are not for the most part persons whose sagacity, character, and judgment one would trust in important matters of worldly concern, from which, indeed, their tastes and occupations commonly cut them off. That the facts of the spiritual world are more real to them than the facts of the natural world they think no disparagement, but a proof of superiority of nature; and they hug the belief that they possess a higher spiritual and a finer moral sense than those persons have who cannot attain to the supernatural illuminations in which they revel.

He who undertakes a frank and critical enquiry will

not fail to note in many instances that those who experience these states of ecstatic coalescence with the Deity have what physicians know and describe as the neurotic temperament, and those who experience them most intensely have that temperament in its most intense degree; its special note being a spasmodic intensity and propensity. Thereby they are pre-disposed to extreme nervous exaltations which trans-late themselves into corresponding states of conscious-ness—into exaggerated, irregular, even perverted sensibilities; into similar exaltations, perversions, and scrupulosities of sentiment and thought before they undergo, and into sublimated states of spiritual ecstasy after they have undergone, the spiritual new birth or conversion by which they enter into com-munion with the Divine; sometimes into oddly nervous, perhaps even spasmodic or convulsive movements.

There is no doubt that so-called swoons or trances or cataleptic seizures befall from time to time persons of a susceptible nervous temperament, especially during the development of the reproductive functions; that such seizures are more easily provoked when the way of them has been made easy by frequent repetitions, so much so that they may then take place at any moment and on the least occasion; that they are attended with a strain of exalted feeling and thought which follows the habit of feeling and thought most nurtured by the individual before their occurrence, whether this has been of spiritually loving or lustful character; that under the delirious strain of feeling the natural consciousness of time and space is much modified, sometimes apparently abolished—as such *formal* conditions of thought must be by dislocations of their mental *forms*; and that all the outward and visible features of these attacks are exactly like those of the nervous seizures which were supposed at one time to bespeak possession by the god, and in some quarters are still thought to be the special means and occasions of divine infusion.

It will suffice here to refer to the varieties of these remarkable seizures—ecstatic, cataleptic, hysteric, hystero-epileptic, and, when induced artificially, hypnotic or mesmeric—without going into a detailed delineation of them. They will be found described at length in their proper places in medical treatises on nervous and mental pathology.* Their general features briefly are—faint, incomplete, almost extinguished consciousness of surroundings; absorption of mind in one strain of purely internal activity, with corresponding strain of vague delirious feeling; insusceptibility, partial or complete, to external impressions; more or less complete abeyance of movement, the muscles of the body or of a part of it being relaxed, or rigidly contracted, or convulsed; acceleration in many cases, in some cases marked lowering, in extreme cases almost suspension, of the organic functions of respiration and circulation. For the time being there is an abeyance of the individual, mental and bodily, as regards his external life of relation; he is, as it were, detached from and dead to the world—whether he is in the body or out of the body he cannot say; but he is not dead wholly, seeing that his organic functions go on at a lowered rate of activity, like those of a hibernating animal, and that his consciousness is absorbed in a purely internal strain of disjointed activity—in a special ecstasy.

Naturally, when he comes to himself he can give no account, in the terms of the language of normal experience, of the singular state of abnormal consciousness in which he was during his ecstasy. Being unlike anything which he ever felt or thought before, it is indescribable in terms of his experience; cannot really be recalled to memory on return to his life of relation, since its very existence means the absence of relations, and to recall it exactly would be to repeat it;

* For such exposition of the more morbid features of mental disorders I may refer to my work on *The Pathology of Mind : a Study of its Distempers, Deformities, and Disorders.*

impossible to be spoken of, except in terms of negation, as something *in*definite, *in*explicable, *in*finite, *in*comprehensible, *in*effable. It stands out from the normal mental life just as a convulsion stands out from the normal bodily life. No wonder, then, that he thinks more than natural, and styles supernatural, a mysterious condition of things which puts him for the time being so incomprehensibly out of himself.

These ecstasies of thought and feeling are easily provoked in persons who, susceptible by nature, have increased their natural susceptibility by practice; the nervous functions falling easily into the habits of their exercise, and very easily into bad habits of exercise in neurotic temperaments, because their innate tendencies are to go off the track: dislocations of mind, like dislocations of body, become easy by practice.

When mind was viewed as a simple, uncompounded, spiritual unity, acting always as a whole in every function of it, such disintegrated states could not well be conceived otherwise than as the work of god or demon which had taken possession of it and constrained it to extranatural displays of function; but now that the mental functions are known to be inseparably connected with nervous substrata disposed and united in the brain in the most orderly fashion, superordinate, co-ordinate, and subordinate— the whole a complex organization of confederate nerve-centres, each capable of more or less independent action—a natural interpretation presents itself. The extraordinary states of mental disintegration evince the separate and irregular function of certain mental nerve-tracts or groups of nerve-tracts, with which goes necessarily a coincident suspension, partial or complete, of the functions of all the rest: the supernatural incubus, therefore, neither demonic nor divine, only morbid. Steadily are the researches of pathology driving the supernatural back into its last and most obscure retreat; for they prove that in the extremest ecstasies there is neither *theolepsy* nor *diabolepsy*, nor any other *lepsy* in the sense of possession of the individual by an external power : what there is truly is a *psycholepsy*.*

This dissolution of mental unity produced by the separate and irregular action of one or more of the numerous and diverse nerve-centres or nerve-tracts which make up the complex unity of the brain has more than an immediate pathological interest. In the first place, such disordinate function is usually the outcome of an innate tendency that way ; it is the individual's evil heritage from a line of ancestral development wanting in solidarity and thorough wholesomeness of character. Secondly, the mental outcome of such want of solidarity, when well marked, is a lack of wholesome unity and veracity of nature in him ; he is never thoroughly at one with himself or in sincere and consistent relations with other persons and things. He is prone to be impressionable, mobile, fluctuating, inconstant in thought and feeling.

* A term one may, perhaps, propose for use as fairly denominating a class of phenomena which call for further and more exact investigation. Several varieties might be formulated and described. For example—

I. Psycholepsy :
    (a) Theological illumination or ecstasy.
    (b) Metaphysical intuition or ecstasy.
    (c) Catalepsy and its allied trances.
    (d) Fanatical transport of enthusiasm or of fury.
    (e) Frenzy of epidemic emotion.
    (f) Fascination of fear.
    (g) Ecstasy of gross brain disease.

SECTION V

THEOLOGICAL ILLUMINATION

PASSING from nervous seizures plainly morbid and from the lessons which they teach, it remains only to consider the nature and value of the latest, best-attested, least-questioned mode of communion with the supernatural—that is, the immediate and actual intuition of God through love of Him.

In order to evoke real feeling in the mind it has been found necessary to represent the Divine in a personal form—as a personal God directly governing the world who concerns Himself with the creatures in it and to whom their prayers and praises may be addressed. Yet an infinite personality is not really a consistent notion to the natural understanding; it is a contradiction in thought and in terms, something like a square circle or a finite infinite; for it is impossible to conceive a personality except under forms of space and time, under which, if infinite and eternal, it cannot be. And how is it possible to love and adore and pray to that which, not coming under the conditions of thought, is inconceivable? This, then, is the unavoidable and awkward dilemma—that, in order to love the infinite it must be personal, and in order to make the personal infinite it must be divested of personality. To the natural man, therefore, the joy of direct internal communion with God is impossible; in order to reach that height of love he must undergo the strange spiritual transformation by which, transcending for the occasion the bounds of personality, he is rapt out of himself. The insoluble problem necessitates two incomprehensible and inconsistent solutions: first, to depersonalize self in order to merge into union with the infinite; secondly, to personalize the infinite in the magnified image of self in order to be into relations with it.

Is, then, the ecstatic love of God which he feels who undergoes the required spiritual transport a genuine state with objective meaning, or is it a mere nervous state with the counterfeit of such meaning? Is the strain of exaltation a subjective dupery owing to a physical process of self-magnetism, or is it the divine effect of a supernatural infusion? That it is induced voluntarily by dwelling with exclusive concentration of thought and feeling on the divine nature and attributes is in conformity with the experience of those who bring on the so-called mesmeric or hypnotic state by concentrating the attention on a single object until they suffer a kind of fascination, as also with the modes in which St. Theresa and other saints achieved their trance-like states of ecstatic rapture. It is certain that a state of special nervous exaltation very like the state of divine ecstasy can be evoked without any other than a simple physical significance; certain also that the disposition of mind studiously invoked and stimulated in order to evoke the divine ecstasy is that best fitted to induce the purely physical state. In no sense is the actual state counterfeit; it is a genuine neurosis, however it be produced and however its accompanying psychosis be interpreted.

Furthermore, a similar nervous ecstasy can be produced experimentally by the use of certain stimulating drugs and vapours. A person may drug as well as think himself into the transcendent rapture. One of the effects of opium, which is the temptation to its habitual use and abuse, is the pleasing state of exaltation of thought and feeling which it engenders in those persons of imaginative temperament who are specially susceptible to its effects: it imparts a genial warmth to the whole being, suffusing the heart with expansive sentiments, stimulating the imagination to ethereal flights, giving large and lofty sweep to the projects of the intellect—necessarily, however, without corresponding power of will to execute them—and even expanding the natural forms of thought by easing or removing the restricting bonds of time and space and conditions. The sense of individual separateness from things seems to dissolve, and the personality to melt into a diffusive oneness with them. The terms of ordinary mental experience are inadequate to describe the expansion of thought and feeling; time, as De Quincey says, lengthens to infinity and space swells to immensity; causality is sublimed into intuition of the relations of things; and other necessary forms of thought seem to fall away from the released mind, or to be so stretched out as to be scarcely sensible to it. Such is the feeling of freedom from the bondage of facts, and such the spacious sense of expansion and well-being that, were the cause of the transport not known, it would certainly be thought to mark an entrance into a higher spiritual sphere.

A still more acute sense of intense mental illumination is produced in some minds by the inhalation of nitrous oxide gas, commonly known as laughing gas. This stimulating effect was experienced by Sir Humphry Davy, who, when he first inhaled it, was astonished at the apparent exaltation of his mental powers, whereby difficulties of thought seemed to vanish as by magic and no subject too difficult of comprehension.

Like intoxicating effects upon the mental functions of the brain are produced by other substances, notably by haschisch, but it is not necessary here to enter into a description of the several effects. Having set forth two plain facts—the physical origin and basis of the state of mental transport in some instances, and the natural production of the physical state by a process of mental induction, the question is whether the state of spiritualization during which the subject is rapt from himself in a divine intuition, although more than ordinary, is ever more than natural. The individual's certitude of the transcendent experience goes for nothing in the matter; it is no greater than that of the mediæval saint who had in her raptures actual visions of God and talked familiarly with Him; while the consent of others is but the consent of those who have inherited the same theological traditions, learned the same special doctrines, breathed the same atmosphere of religious sentiment, observed the same rites of worship, and assiduously trained their nervous systems to the same habits of exercise.

The terms *ecstasy* and *rapture*, which are in use to describe the extraordinary mental transport, are instructive when they are traced back to their origin and etymological meaning. *Ecstasy* means literally a standing out of self (ἔκ στάσις), and *rapture* the state of one who is rapt or carried away from himself; and, inasmuch as the soul was the self, there was nothing for it in olden times but to presume that this was done by a supernatural power, divine or diabolic, which had taken possession of it. The original meaning of the terms has still a large measure of applicability if the theory be true that a certain order of nerve-tracts is thrown into a state of ultra-physiological activity, of almost delirious or convulsive character, in which they are cut off from functional connections with their associated nerve-tracts; standing out, in a rapt function, they are thereby severed from the ordinary operations of reason and will which, as consciousness is absorbed in the ecstasy, are suspended.

When the disintegration is past and the individual returns to his integrated self, he does not exhibit much trace of his extra-natural experience. How can he now, when he is himself, not the other and translated self? The more intense and delirious the spiritual ecstasy, the more completely does it stand outside his ordinary life and character as an event apart. He may be compared to one who, having been in a hypnotic or an epileptic state of abnormal consciousness, forgets nearly or entirely, when he comes to himself, all that he thought and felt during it, or at best remembers it dreamily and remotely only as having happened to a self so estranged as not to seem his. It is no surprise, therefore, that those who undergo these heroic ecstasies are not more holy than other persons : not more patient, sincere, self-denying, and habitually considerate for others in the prosaic struggles and trials of daily life. The simple truth is that they usually show less disciplined self-control, less quiet self-renunciation, less patient forbearance, less prudent foresight, and less store of the homely virtues which, not suiting the lofty exaltations of the spiritual temperament, nevertheless make the daily happiness of others.

In face of the claim to superfine spiritual sense and moral feeling made by persons who profess and practise divine intoxication, it is right to take strict scientific account of their lives and characters simply as facts of observation, in order to judge how far these verify their pretensions. The facts do not verify the pretensions; all that they verify is the intensity of a tender self-love.

Without doubt individuals among them sometimes deserve great moral credit for persistent and pains-taking endeavours, by straining after spiritual illu-mination, consciously to avoid the inconstancies and unveracities of thought and feeling into which it is the bent of their peculiarly constructed minds, predisposed to delirious ecstacies of thought and feeling, to plunge them; but for them, as for others, it is impossible to eradicate nature, whose fundamental note of frailty is a want of thorough unity and balance of mental con-stitution. Just therefore is the scruple to accept the intuitive certitude of their sentiment as indisputable, whose opinions in all other relations of life are very disputable; just, too, the reason which holds the common sense of the race, in a matter open to common experience, to be much more trustworthy than the uncommon sense which they affect.

The solid test of wholesome feeling is its capability of expenditure in good thought and action. Not the laboured thinking of high thoughts, nor the forced feeling of fine feelings, nor the tortured ingenuity to express them in strains of elaborate eloquence, but the thinking and doing definitely for his kind it is which best develops sympathetic feelings and human instincts of a manly and wholesome type. The effect of the habitual indulgence of emotion divorced from activity, or in excess of the proper activity, is self-deception and hypocrisy, conscious or unconscious; it is egoistic intoxication masquerading as altruistic emotion, with an incapacity of corresponding self-sacrifice in conduct. The preacher who spends effusive emotion in strains of elaborately concocted eloquence actually demoralizes his understanding. To act well in thoroughly adaptive reflex function to the social environment is the right way to keep sensibilities and feelings in due bounds and proportion; for just as doing imparts real meaning to language, which without it is apt to be vague, confused, and equivocal, so it compresses and utilizes, in order to form fruit, the emotional energy whose unrestrained tendency is to run into luxuriant display of empty rhetoric, of which comes little or no fruit in homely good works, but, instead, much talk of self-denial along with incontinent self-abuse of sentiment. Is *uninformed* emotion any better really than uninformed understanding? frenzy of feeling worth more than frenzy of thought?

SECTION VI

THEOLOGY AND METAPHYSICS

IF a knowledge of nature by the method of observation and reflection be irreconcilably opposed to, and vitally incompatible with, any knowledge of it or of a supernature by a method of pure internal intuition—the two methods by their principles doomed to a truceless conflict—it is not the less true that the latter method may claim the countenance and aid of metaphysics. The metaphysical method rests on much the same footing as the method of theological intuition—namely, the intending of the mind not to things but to nothings. Shutting his eyes and closing his ears to what is outside him, suspending, in fact, the functions of sense and of reflection on that which the senses supply, his mind withdrawn from all outward distractions into a pure internal contemplation of itself and its forms of activity, the supreme metaphysician, like the theologian, goes far finally to achieve a process of self-magnetization—a self-absorption detached from things of sense—which is the counterpart of the theological ecstasy; and in that detached state of sublimed thought, out of which substance has been volatilized, he has access to the inmost and highest secrets of being—is at home with supreme substance, the thing in itself, the absolute ego, free-will, intuitions of pure reason, infinite space and time, infinite perfection, the identification of opposites, and like supersensual strains of formless thought.*

* How can absolute knowledge in a relative being be knowledge at all? Is not the supposed absoluteness of thought or feeling the surest proof of its individuality—its separateness, that is, from the whole—and therefore of its defect or falsity?

If these states are truly revelations of supreme truths, then the mental weaklings who cannot perform them, and perceive not their transcendent value, are beings of inferior mental endowment who merit the sort of pity bestowed on the blind man by those who have the use of their eyes; but if, on the other hand, they are the objectivations of straining ineptitudes, subjective duperies only, then he who performs them may be likened to one who, having thrown his muscles into a cataleptic rigidity, and thus divested their movements of all form and purpose as natural function, feels the formless activity achieved, unlike as it is to all his ordinary experience, to be supernatural and divine.

The induction of such a metaphysical strain of thought is naturally the more successful the more free the mind is from the consolidating acquisitions of positive knowledge of nature and practical experience of men and things, and the more it has accustomed itself by practice to the stimulation of self-absorbing ecstasies of substance-lacking thought. Theology and metaphysics are instinctive allies, and may still count upon one another for mutual aid and comfort in offensive and defensive alliance. Unhappily, their long union has been a union of fruitless embraces.

Now, it is certain that a great idealism of any sort, like any theory not entirely baseless, may always find points of support in the multitudinous analogies afforded by the changing aspects and various facets of nature, and that whoever goes to work to build it up synthetically by diligently seeking assimilable relations in every quarter, and wittingly or unwittingly turning away from every fact which conflicts with or contradicts its principle and cannot be used to help its growth, may succeed in building a very imposing edifice. All the more so when he entangles himself and his followers in ill-defined and equivocal phraseology. Any number of pretentious philosophical structures may be raised in that way;

and to the greater height the greater the ingenuity and industry of their architects in seeking the material which they want, and in rejecting that which they want not, for their building purposes. But the way is not the way of true knowledge, and the structures so built are artificial and frail in the end.

Any system, philosophical or theological, so built up, be it never so lofty and imposing, is no better than the meanest theory framed on a similar system—it is essentially a structure apart from the living body of true knowledge, not an organic part of it. Neither goodness of intention, nor grandeur of design, nor ingenuity of construction, nor devotion of disciples, can save it from the necessity of strict verification by observation and induction, nor make up for what it lacks if it fails to stand that test.

Not by standing out of nature in the ecstasies of rapt and overstrained idealisms of any sort, but by large and close converse with nature and human nature in all their moods, aspects, and relations, is the basis of fruitful ideals and sound mental development laid in every domain of thought. In the end the speculative philosopher who, lacking the necessary basis of positive experience, thinks out systems of the universe in his closet, is no better employed than was the poet of old when he constructed a variety of ingenious myths to explain the causes of things, or than is the theologian who works himself into artificial states of spiritual transport in relation to unknown inhabitants of infinity and eternity. Theologian and philosopher alike exhibit the strained functions of a sort of *psycholepsy*: the one in the futile folly of striving to discover and expound the *first principles* of things; the other in the equally futile folly of striving to divine and describe the creation of them. Creations and first principles are not things of human concern.

Of every valid human thought and feeling—of all genuine knowledge—it is true to say that it represents, directly or indirectly, the formation of a complete and fit circuit between the individual and nature. Instead of labouring patiently to effect fit interrelation in every case and to restore the contact when interrupted, the transcendental metaphysician strains earnestly to break circuit by severing himself from the outward fact and relations; aims to make the interruption more and more complete by his convulsive inner straining; does all he can to hinder the restoration of the natural condition. However much he esteem and extol his method and its results— and the delirious sense of freedom and power in the stimulation of function without form and void inevitably leads him to overrate it—his ecstatic achievements of thought and feeling, whether theological or metaphysical, are entirely personal; they have no objective value, no voucher of validity for any other person; there is not the smallest proof that they are of any more worth than the ecstatic, hysteric, cataleptic, and like raptures which they resemble.